Conversion Tables of Units
in Science & Engineering

Conversion Tables of Units in Science & Engineering

Ari L. Horvath

Imperial Chemical Industries PLC,
Mond Division,
Runcorn,
Cheshire, UK

First published 1986 by
THE MACMILLAN PRESS LTD
London and Basingstoke

Associated companies in Auckland, Delhi, Dublin, Gaborone, Hamburg, Harare, Hong Kong, Johannesburg, Kuala Lumpur, Lagos, Manzini, Melbourne, Mexico City, Nairobi, New York, Singapore, Tokyo

British Library Cataloguing in Publication Data

Conversion tables of units in science &
engineering.
1. Science—Handbooks, manuals, etc.
2. Engineering—Handbooks, manuals, etc.
I. Horvath, Ari L.
502′.12 Q199

ISBN 0-333-40857-8

Phototypeset by Styleset Ltd, Warminster, Wiltshire
Printed in Great Britain

Contents

Preface

This book was planned to contain an up-to-date collection of conversion factors used in science and engineering. To achieve this, taking into account the variety of subjects, the contents have been divided into tables with conversion factors and alphabetical list of quantities that are not common today.

It has appeared useful to devote only one special table to each quantity and to include only the relevant conversion factors; those units that are only of historical interest are listed separately in alphabetical order. It is hoped, that, in general, a proper balance between these two formats of presentation has been achieved so as to make the book useful to most practising scientists and engineers.

The author wishes to acknowledge the aid of his colleagues and, in particular, the help of those who read, criticized and provided helpful comments to improve the contents and presentation of this book. The author would also like to thank Mr John E. Colchester, Division Technical Manager, for his interest and approval of this compilation. Thanks are due to Imperial Chemical Industries PLC for permission to publish this book.

I am very grateful to my wife Joan for her real help and patience during the preparation of the manuscript.

December 1985 Ari L. Horvath

Introduction

This book of conversion tables is intended for students, scientists (physical, medical, etc.) and engineers (mechanical, electrical, civil, chemical, etc.) with diverse backgrounds. This collection of tables from many sources and diverse areas has been carefully selected and purposefully presented in a simple and effective way.

The objective of this monograph is to collect, compile and present the conversion factors among the relevant units used in education, design, and research and development during the daily activities in industry and related enterprises. The book has been written from a technical perspective and provides a complete and critical coverage of the conversion factors. It is devoted to one of the most important problems confronting design engineers and scientists during their working days. It is hoped that the book will also serve as a companion for engineering and science students throughout their academic years.

Despite the numerous conversion tables available in various technical books and specialist publications, there is a need for a compilation with users' requirements in mind. This book is very concise without losing its clarity and easy understanding of the conversions between the various units. The conversion tables have been compiled after careful consideration of that need. This compilation will provide the most practical answers to the queries of engineers and scientists in connection with conversion of the widely spread units in the published literature. The user will find an easy access to the conversion factors without looking for and searching into various handbooks.

The presentation of the conversion factors is entirely in tables with a diagonal equality in each horizontal and vertical column. There is no doubt that this type of tabulation can provide the most effective and easily understood conversion between various units and quantities.

Despite the great efforts by governments and various international organizations to introduce and adopt the International System of Units (better known as SI units) in most countries, progress has been slow and persuasion is not effective, particularly economically. The International System of Units (le Système international d'Unités) was agreed during the 11th General Conference of Weights and Measures (*Comptes Rendus des Séances de la onziéme Conference général des Poids et Measures*, Oct. 1960, p. 87 (Paris, Gauthie–Villiers)), and has now been adopted by most countries of the world. The SI units consist of seven basic quantities: length, mass, time, electric current, thermodynamic temperature, amount of substance and luminous intensity. The General Conference also made recommendations for the rules for the prefixes, the derived and supplementary units and other matters. It is intended to adopt the SI units throughout the world in educational circles, science, technology, industry and commerce. Its universal use avoids confusion in international trade and scientific work.

The teaching and understanding of the SI units in schools are the most important aspects of the success. Advice on the correct use of SI terminology, from the simple to the complex, is available in various publications on SI units. The necessary guidelines are available in technical documents or special books.

The commercial and technical literature is still written in various units, and it will take a considerable time to perform all writings in SI units only. The already written information in books, journals and documents cannot be altered and the availability of conversion factors is necessary to understand and convert the old units and measurements into SI units.

This compilation of conversion factors covers a very wide area of interest to students and adults. The following main sections of units and quantities are covered:

1) mechanical units
2) thermodynamic quantities
3) units of light
4) units of electricity
5) units of magnetism
6) units of acoustics
7) units of radiation

For systematic calculations on data from many sources, self-consistent conversion factors are highly desirable. A revised set of conversion factors and defined values based on the values accepted by specialists is therefore used in this compilation.

The units and conversion factors presented in this compilation are based on well-established reference sources, which are listed at the end of the book under the list of references.

Part 1

Definitions and Conversion of Units

Fundamental physical constants

There are three major systems of units of measurement often found in the published literature (i.e. books, journals and documents in general):

1) imperial or British system
2) metric system
   cgs (centimeter/gram/second) system
   mks (meter/kilogram/second) system
3) SI System (le Système international d'Unités)

The imperial system of units has been developed and used in the UK and Commonwealth countries. It is based on the yard, pound and second. The metric system originated in France during the 18th century. Since 1876 the Conférence Générale des Poids et Mesures (CGPM) has been the ruling organization for all aspects of units and measurements. The two systems introduced, cgs and mks, are now of historical interest.

The SI unit of measurements was proposed by the CGPM in 1971 and since it has become the standard system of units in most countries. The system is based on the seven base units listed in Table 1.1.

The seven SI base units have been defined by the CGPM as follows:

1) Unit of length—meter (m)
The meter is the length equal to 1 650 763.73 wavelengths in vacuum of the radiation corresponding to the transition between the level $2p_{10} - 5d_5$ of the krypton-86 atom.

2) Unit of mass—kilogram (kg)
The international prototype of the kilogram is kept at the Bureau International des Poids et Mesures under specified conditions. The prototype is made of platinum-iridium alloy.

3) Unit of time—second (s)
The second is the duration of 9 192 631 770 periods of the radiation corresponding to the transition between the two hyperfine levels of the ground state of the cesium-133 atom.

4) Unit of electric current—ampere (A)
The ampere is that constant current which, if maintained in two straight parallel conductors of infinite length, of negligible circular cross-section, and placed 1 meter apart in vacuum, would produce between these conductors a force equal to 2×10^{-7} newton per meter of length.

5) Unit of thermodynamic temperature—kelvin (K)
The kelvin is based on the triple point of water as the fundamental fixed point. The kelvin is the fraction 1/273.16 of the thermodynamic temperature of the triple point of water.

The unit kelvin and its symbol K are also used to express an interval or a difference of temperature. However, the unit of degree Celsius (symbol: °C) or a difference of Celsius temperature may also be used.

6) Unit of amount of substance—mole (mol)
The mole is the amount of substance of a system that contains as many elementary entities as there are atoms in 0.012 kilogram of carbon-12. When the mole is used, the elementary entities must be specified and may be atoms, molecules, ions, electrons, other particles or specified groups of such particles.

Table 1.1. SI base units

Quantity	Symbol for quantity	Base unit	Symbol for unit
length	l	meter	m
mass	m	kilogram	kg
time	t	second	s
electric current	I	ampere	A
thermodynamic temperature	T	kelvin	K
amount of substance	n	mole	mol
luminous intensity	I_v	candela	cd

Table 1.2. Derived SI units

Name of SI units	Symbol	Physical quantity	Definition of SI unit
becquerel	Bq	radioactivity	s^{-1}
coulomb	C	electric charge	A s
farad	F	electric capacitance	$A^2\ s^4\ kg^{-1}\ m^{-2}$ (= A s V^{-1})
gray	Gy	absorbed dose	$m^2\ s^{-2}$ (= J kg^{-1})
henry	H	inductance	$m^2\ kg\ s^{-2}\ A^{-2}$ (= V A^{-1} s)
hertz	Hz	frequency	s^{-1}
joule	J	energy, work	$m^2\ kg\ s^{-2}$
lumen	lm	luminous flux	cd sr
lux	lx	illumination	cd sr m^{-2}
newton	N	force	m kg s^{-2}
ohm	Ω	electric resistance	kg $m^2\ A^{-2}\ s^{-3}$ (= V A^{-1})
pascal	Pa	pressure	kg $m^{-1}\ s^{-2}$ (= N m^{-2})
siemens	S	electric conductance	$A^2\ s^3\ kg^{-1}\ m^{-2}$ (= A V^{-1})
steradian	sr	solid angle	$m^2\ m^{-2}$
tesla	T	magnetic flux density	kg $A^{-1}\ s^{-2}$ (= V s m^{-2})
volt	V	electric potential difference	m^2 kg $A^{-1}\ s^{-3}$ (= J $A^{-1}\ s^{-1}$)
watt	W	power	m^2 kg s^{-3} (= J s^{-1})
weber	Wb	magnetic flux	m^2 kg $A^{-1}\ s^{-2}$ (= V s)

7) Unit of luminous intensity—candela (cd)
The candela is the luminous intensity, in the perpendicular direction, of a surface of 1/600 000 square meter of a black body at the temperature of freezing platinum under a pressure of 101 325 newton per square meter.

The coherent units of the system based on these base units may be used to express SI-derived units. Several derived units have special names and symbols. They are listed in Table 1.2.

In addition to the base and derived units the 11th Conference Generale des Poids et Measures introduced a third class of SI units called supplementary units. Both units—radian (plane angle) and steradian (solid angle)—belong to the class of SI supplementary units. However, they may be regarded either as base units or as derived units.

The prefix symbols (*see* Table 1.3) indicate the decimal multiples and sub-multiples of the SI units. An exponent affixed to a symbol containing a prefix indicates that the multiple or sub-multiple of the symbol is raised to the power expressed by the exponent.

Table 1.3. Prefixes

Decimal equivalent	Prefix	Symbol	Exponential expression
1 000 000 000 000	tera	T	10^{12}
1 000 000 000	giga	G	10^9
1 000 000	mega	M	10^6
1 000	kilo	k	10^3
100	hecto	h	10^2
10	deka	da	10
0.1	deci	d	10^{-1}
0.01	centi	c	10^{-2}
0.001	milli	m	10^{-3}
0.000 001	micro	μ	10^{-6}
0.000 000 001	nano	n	10^{-9}
0.000 000 000 001	pico	p	10^{-12}
0.000 000 000 000 001	femto	f	10^{-15}
0.000 000 000 000 000 001	atto	a	10^{-18}

Table 1.4. Fundamental physical constants

Physical quantity	Value	SI unit
atomic mass unit	$1.660\,565\,5 \times 10^{-27}$	kg
Avogadro constant	$6.022\,045 \times 10^{23}$	mol^{-1}
Bohr magneton	$9.274\,078 \times 10^{-24}$	$J\,T^{-1}$
Bohr radius	$5.291\,770\,6 \times 10^{-11}$	m
Boltzmann constant	$1.380\,662 \times 10^{-23}$	$J\,K^{-1}$
charge of proton (elementary charge)	$1.602\,189\,2 \times 10^{-19}$	C
charge to mass ratio for electron	$1.758\,804\,7 \times 10^{11}$	$C\,kg^{-1}$
curie	3.7×10^{10}	disintegrations s^{-1}
Einstein constant	$8.987\,551\,79 \times 10^{16}$	$J\,kg^{-1}$
electron magnetic moment	$9.284\,832 \times 10^{-24}$	$J\,T^{-1}$
electron radius, classical	$2.817\,938 \times 10^{-15}$	m
electron rest mass	$9.109\,534 \times 10^{-31}$	kg
electron volt	$1.602\,189\,2 \times 10^{-19}$	J
electronic charge	$1.602\,189\,2 \times 10^{-19}$	C
Faraday constant	$9.648\,456 \times 10^{4}$	$C\,mol^{-1}$
fine structure constant	$7.297\,350\,6 \times 10^{-3}$	—
first radiation constant	$3.741\,832 \times 10^{-16}$	$W\,m^{2}$
gas constant	8.314 41	$J\,mol^{-1}\,K^{-1}$
gravitational acceleration	9.806 65	$m\,s^{-2}$
gravitational constant	6.672×10^{-11}	$N\,m^{2}\,kg^{-2}$
Hartree energy	$4.359\,814 \times 10^{-18}$	J
ice-point temperature	273.15	K
Lande g-factor for free electron	2.002 319 313 4	—
Loschmidt constant	$2.686\,754 \times 10^{25}$	m^{-3}
magnetic flux quantum	$2.067\,850\,6 \times 10^{-15}$	$J\,s\,C^{-1}$
molar volume of ideal gas at stp	0.022 413 83	$m^{3}\,mol^{-1}$
Muon rest mass	$1.883\,566 \times 10^{-28}$	kg
neutron rest mass	$1.674\,954\,3 \times 10^{-27}$	kg
normal atmosphere	$1.013\,25 \times 10^{5}$	$N\,m^{-2}$
nuclear magneton	$5.050\,824 \times 10^{-27}$	$J\,T^{-1}$
permeability of vacuum	$4\pi \times 10^{-7}$	$J\,s^{2}\,C^{-2}\,m^{-1}$ (= $H\,m^{-1}$)
permittivity of vacuum	$8.854\,187\,82 \times 10^{-12}$	$J^{-1}\,C^{2}\,m^{-1}$ ($F\,m^{-1}$)
Planck constant	$6.626\,176 \times 10^{-34}$	J s
proton gyromagnetic ratio	$2.675\,198\,7 \times 10^{8}$	$s^{-1}\,T^{-1}$
proton magnetic moment	$1.410\,617\,1 \times 10^{-26}$	$J\,T^{-1}$
proton rest mass	$1.672\,648\,5 \times 10^{-27}$	kg
Rydberg constant	$1.097\,373\,177 \times 10^{7}$	m^{-1}
second radiation constant	0.014 387 86	m K
speed of light in vacuum	$2.997\,924\,58 \times 10^{8}$	$m\,s^{-1}$
standard acceleration of free fall	9.806 65	$m\,s^{-2}$
standard molar volume of ideal gas (273.15 K, 101 325 $N\,m^{-2}$)	0.022 413 83	$m^{3}\,mol^{-1}$
standard pressure	$1.013\,25 \times 10^{5}$	$N\,m^{-2}$
standard temperature	273.15	K
Stefan–Boltzmann constant	$5.670\,32 \times 10^{-8}$	$W\,m^{-2}\,K^{-4}$
Thomson cross-section	$6.652\,447 \times 10^{-28}$	m^{2}
triple point of water	273.15	K
Wien's radiation constant	$2.897\,790 \times 10^{-3}$	m K

Table 1.5. Atomic weights of the elements

Name	Symbol	Atomic number	Atomic weight
actinium	Ac	89	227.028
aluminum	Al	13	26.981 54
americium	Am	95	243.0
antimony (stibium)	Sb	51	121.75
argon	Ar	18	39.948
arsenic	As	33	74.9216
astatine	At	85	210.0
barium	Ba	56	137.33
berkelium	Bk	97	247.0
beryllium	Be	4	9.012 18
bismuth	Bi	83	208.9804
boron	B	5	10.811
bromine	Br	35	79.904
cadmium	Cd	48	112.41
cesium	Cs	55	132.9054
calcium	Ca	20	40.078
californium	Cf	98	251.0
carbon	C	6	12.011
cerium	Ce	58	140.12
chlorine	Cl	17	35.453
chromium	Cr	24	51.9961
cobalt	Co	27	58.9332
copper	Cu	29	63.546
curium	Cm	96	247.0
dysprosium	Dy	66	162.50
einsteinium	Es	99	252.0
element 108	—	108	—
erbium	Er	68	167.26
europium	Eu	63	151.96
fermium	Fm	100	257.0
fluorine	F	9	18.998 403
francium	Fr	87	223.0
gadolinium	Gd	64	157.25
gallium	Ga	31	69.723
germanium	Ge	32	72.59
gold (aurum)	Au	79	196.9665
hafnium	Hf	72	178.49
helium	He	2	4.002 602
holmium	Ho	67	164.9304
hydrogen	H	1	1.007 94
indium	In	49	114.82
iodine	I	53	126.9045
iridium	Ir	77	192.22
iron (ferrum)	Fe	26	55.847
krypton	Kr	36	83.80
lanthanum	La	57	138.9055
lawrencium	Lr	103	260.0
lead (plumbum)	Pb	82	207.2
lithium	Li	3	6.941
lutetium	Lu	71	174.967
magnesium	Mg	12	24.305
manganese	Mn	25	54.9380
mendelevium	Md	101	258.0
mercury (hygragyrum)	Hg	80	200.59
molybdenum	Mo	42	95.94

Table 1.5 (*contd*)

Name	Symbol	Atomic number	Atomic weight
neodymium	Nd	60	144.24
neon	Ne	10	20.179
neptunium	Np	93	237.0482
nickel	Ni	28	58.69
niobium	Nb	41	92.9064
nitrogen	N	7	14.0067
nobelium	No	102	259.0
osmium	Os	76	190.2
oxygen	O	8	15.9994
palladium	Pd	46	106.42
phosphorus	P	15	30.973 76
platinum	Pt	78	195.08
plutonium	Pu	94	239.13
polonium	Po	84	209.0
potassium (kalium)	K	19	39.0983
praseodymium	Pr	59	140.9077
promethium	Pm	61	145.0
protactinium	Pa	91	231.036
radium	Ra	88	226.025
radon	Rn	86	222.0
rhenium	Re	75	186.207
rhodium	Rh	45	102.9055
rubidium	Rb	37	85.4678
ruthenium	Ru	44	101.07
samarium	Sm	62	150.36
scandium	Sc	21	44.955 91
selenium	Se	34	78.96
silicon	Si	14	28.0855
silver (argentum)	Ag	47	107.8682
sodium (natrium)	Na	11	22.989 77
strontium	Sr	38	87.62
sulfur	S	16	32.066
tantalum	Ta	73	180.9479
technetium	Tc	43	98.9062
tellurium	Te	52	127.60
terbium	Tb	65	158.9254
thallium	Tl	81	204.383
thorium	Th	90	232.0381
thulium	Tm	69	168.9342
tin (stannum)	Sn	50	118.710
titanium	Ti	22	47.88
tungsten (wolfram)	W	74	183.85
unnilqualium	Unq[a]	104	261.0
unnilpentium	Unp[a]	105	262.0
unnilhexium	Unh[a]	106	263.0
unnilseptium	Uns[a]	107	262.0
uranium	U	92	238.0289
vanadium	V	23	50.9415
xenon	Xe	54	131.29
ytterbium	Yb	70	173.04
yttrium	Y	39	88.9059
zinc	Zn	30	65.39
zirconium	Zr	40	91.224

[a] Symbols based on IUPAC systematic names.

Table 1.6. Periodic table of the elements

Group: New notation	1	2	3	4	5	6	7	8	9	10	11	12	13	14	15	16	17	18
Previous IUPAC form	IA	IIA	IIIA	IVA	VA	VIA	VIIA	VIIIA	VIIIA	VIIIA			IIIB	IVB	VB	VIB	VIIB	VIIIA
CAS version			IIIB	IVB	VB	VIB	VIIB	VIII	VIII	VIII	IB	IIB	IIIA	IVA	VA	VIA	VIIA	
	1 H																	2 He
	3 Li	4 Be											5 B	6 C	7 N	8 O	9 F	10 Ne
	11 Na	12 Mg											13 Al	14 Si	15 P	16 S	17 Cl	18 Ar
	19 K	20 Ca	21 Sc	22 Ti	23 V	24 Cr	25 Mn	26 Fe	27 Co	28 Ni	29 Cu	30 Zn	31 Ga	32 Ge	33 As	34 Se	35 Br	36 Kr
	37 Rb	38 Sr	39 Y	40 Zr	41 Nb	42 Mo	43 Tc	44 Ru	45 Rh	46 Pd	47 Ag	48 Cd	49 In	50 Sn	51 Sb	52 Te	53 I	54 Xe
	55 Cs	56 Ba	57 La ★	72 Hf	73 Ta	74 W	75 Re	76 Os	77 Ir	78 Pt	79 Au	80 Hg	81 Tl	82 Pb	83 Bi	84 Po	85 At	86 Rn
	87 Fr	88 Ra	89 Ac ▲	104 Unq[a]	105 Unp[a]	106 Unh[a]	107 Uns[a]											

★ Lanthanide series	58 Ce	59 Pr	60 Nd	61 Pm	62 Sm	63 Eu	64 Gd	65 Tb	66 Dy	67 Ho	68 Er	69 Tm	70 Yb	71 Lu
▲ Actinide series	90 Th	91 Pa	92 U	93 Np	94 Pu	95 Am	96 Cm	97 Bk	98 Cf	99 Es	100 Fm	101 Md	102 No	103 Lr

[a] Symbols based on IUPAC systematic names.

Part 2

Conversion Factors

2.1 Length (m)

The length as a quantity is often described by an alternative word. The following terms are used:

altitude
breadth
depth
diameter
displacement
distance
height
line segment
path length
radial distance
radius
thickness
wavelength
width

Some of the units listed in Table 2.1a are not specific and require further details: for example, 1 mile might be imperial, geographical, sea, etc. To avoid any confusion, it is recommended that full details on the unit used (e.g., 1 mile (telegraph nautical)) are given.

The units of length listed in Table 2.1a have been taken from the published literature (*see* References). This table provides the conversion factors to meter, which is the SI unit for length. Interconversion factors for the common units of length are given in Table 2.1b.

2.2 Area (m^2)

Area is an enclosed surface or region. There are several formulas for calculating areas enclosed by a definitely bounded piece of surrounding. The common forms of areas are:

rectangle
square
triangle
trapezoid
parallelogram
regular pentagon
regular hexagon
regular octagon
circle

There are several units of area. These quantities are often expressed in terms of the squares of any of the units of length listed in Table 2.1a.

The traditional UK and US units of area and their relationship to the square meter (SI unit) have been compiled from the literature and listed in Table 2.2a. The interconversion factors for the common units of area are presented in Table 2.2b.

2.3 Volume (capacity) (m^3)

Volume is defined as the amount of space occupied by a body, measured and expressed in cubic units. The units of volume or capacity are often expressed in terms of the cubics of any of the units of length listed in Table 2.1a.

There is no distinction between volume and capacity in the SI systems of unit. However, the metric system changed between 1901 and 1964. The definitions for liter are

$$1 \text{ liter } (1901) = 1.000\,028 \text{ liter } (1964)$$

Since 1964, the liter has been redefined as one cubic decimeter (as before 1901)

$$1 \text{ liter } (1964) = 1 \text{ cubic decimeter}$$

The various conversion factors of units of volume are presented in Tables 2.3a and 2.3b.

One Amagat unit of volume is defined as the volume occupied by 1 mole of a real gas at 0°C and 1 atm pressure. Despite a slight deviation between real and perfect (or ideal) gases at this condition, the Amagat unit of volume may be calculated as

$$1 \text{ Amagat unit of volume} = 0.022\,413\,6 \text{ m}^3 \text{ mol}^{-1}$$

The Amagat unit of volume is the reciprocal of the Amagat unit of density

$$1 \text{ Amagat unit of volume} = \frac{1}{\text{Amagat unit of density}}$$

thus

$$1 \text{ Amagat unit of density} = 44.615\,77 \text{ mol m}^{-3}$$

One Berlin unit of volume is defined as the volume occupied by 1 mole of a real gas at 0°C and 1 meter of mercury pressure.

The virial coefficients B and C are given as $\text{cm}^3\ \text{mol}^{-1}$ and $\text{cm}^6\ \text{mol}^{-2}$, respectively, in cgs units. The conversion factors to SI units are as follows:

$$B\ (\text{cm}^3\ \text{mol}^{-1}) = 1.0 \times 10^{-6}\ B\ (\text{m}^3\ \text{mol}^{-1})$$

$$C\ (\text{cm}^6\ \text{mol}^{-2}) = 1.0 \times 10^{-12}\ C\ (\text{m}^6\ \text{mol}^{-2})$$

Table 2.1a. Miscellaneous units of length

Unit	m
1 ångström (or tenth meter or rowland) (A)	1.0×10^{-10}
1 astronomical unit (au)	1.496×10^{11}
1 atomic unit of length	$5.291\,67 \times 10^{-11}$
1 barleycorn	$8.466\,67 \times 10^{-3}$
1 bicron (or stigma)	1.0×10^{-12}
1 Bohr radius	5.3×10^{-9}
1 bolt	36.576
1 cable length	
0.1 UK nautical mile	185.318
100 fathoms	182.88
120 fathoms	219.456
1 caliber	2.54×10^{-4}
1 cascade unit (or radiation length or radiation unit)	159.424 (in air)
1 centimeter (cm)	0.01
1 chain	
Gunter's or surveyor's	20.1168
nautical	4.572
Ramden's or engineer's	30.48
1 cubit	0.4572
1 cut	274.319 52
1 decimeter (dm)	0.1
1 dekameter (dam)	10.0
1 digit	0.019 05
1 douziéme	$1.763\,89 \times 10^{-4}$
1 ell	
Flemish	0.6858
French	1.3716
UK	1.1430
1 em (printer's, pica)	$4.233\,33 \times 10^{-3}$
1 fathom	1.8288
1 fermi	1.0×10^{-15}
1 foot (ft)	
cape	0.314 858
international	0.3048
US or survey	0.304 800 6
1 French foot	0.324 85
1 furlong	201.168
1 gigameter (Gm)	1.0×10^{9}
1 goad	1.3716
1 hand	0.1016
1 hank	768.094 664
1 hectometer (hm)	100.0
1 heer	548.639 046
1 inch (in)	0.0254
1 iron	$5.291\,67 \times 10^{-4}$
1 kilometer (km)	1.0×10^{3}
1 kxu (or siegbahn, 1000 X units)	$1.002\,020\,1 \times 10^{-10}$
1 lea	109.727 809
1 league	
nautical, imperial	$5.559\,552 \times 10^{3}$
nautical, international	5.556×10^{3}
statue	$4.828\,032 \times 10^{3}$
1 light year	9.4605×10^{15}
1 ligne	$2.116\,67 \times 10^{-3}$
1 line	
imperial	$2.116\,66 \times 10^{-3}$
metric	1.0×10^{-3}
US	6.35×10^{-4}

Table 2.1a (contd)

Unit	m
1 link	
Gunter's or surveyor's	0.201 168
Ramden's or engineer's	0.3048
1 megameter (Mm)	1.0×10^{6}
1 meter (m)	1.0
1 micrometer (μm)	1.0×10^{-6}
1 micromicro	1.0×10^{-12}
1 micron (or micrometer) (μm)	1.0×10^{-6}
1 mil	2.54×10^{-5}
1 mile	
geographical	$1.853\ 184 \times 10^{3}$
imperial	$1.609\ 344 \times 10^{3}$
nautical, imperial	$1.853\ 184 \times 10^{3}$
nautical, international	1.852×10^{3}
sea	1.8288×10^{3}
telegraph nautical	$1.855\ 317\ 6 \times 10^{3}$
1 millimeter (mm)	1.0×10^{-3}
1 millimicron (or nanometer) (nm)	1.0×10^{-9}
1 myriameter	1.0×10^{4}
1 nail	0.057 15
1 nanometer (or millimicron) (nm)	1.0×10^{-9}
1 ounce	$3.968\ 75 \times 10^{-4}$
1 pace (military)	0.762
1 palm	0.0762
1 Paris inch (or pounce)	0.027 069 973
1 parsec	$3.085\ 72 \times 10^{16}$
1 perch (or rod or pole)	5.0292
1 pica (printer's)	$4.217\ 517\ 6 \times 10^{-3}$
1 piece	9.143 984
1 pied (or French foot)	0.324 85
1 point (printer's)	0.351×10^{-3}
1 pole (or perch or rod)	5.0292
1 pouce (or Paris inch)	0.027 069 973
1 quadrant	1.0×10^{7}
1 quarter	0.228 60
1 radiation length (or cascade unit or radiation unit)	159.424 (in air)
1 rod (or perch or pole)	5.0292
1 rope (imperial)	6.096
1 rowland (or ångström or tenth meter)	1.0×10^{-10}
1 second	$2.116\ 67 \times 10^{-3}$
1 siegbahn unit (or X-ray unit or X unit)	$1.002\ 02 \times 10^{-13}$
1 sirometer	1.496×10^{17}
1 skein	109.728
1 span	0.2286
1 spat	1.0×10^{12}
1 spindle	$1.316\ 733\ 71 \times 10^{4}$
1 stab	1.0
1 stigma (or bicron)	1.0×10^{-12}
1 tenth meter (or ångström or rowland)	1.0×10^{-10}
1 thou	2.54×10^{-5}
1 thread	1.371 597 6
1 wavelength of orange-red line of krypton-86	$6.057\ 802\ 11 \times 10^{-7}$
1 wavelength of red line of cadmium	$6.438\ 469\ 6 \times 10^{-7}$
1 X unit (or siegbahn unit)	$1.002\ 02 \times 10^{-13}$
1 yard (yd)	
imperial	0.914 398 41
scientific	0.9144
US	0.914 401 83

Table 2.1b. Length interconversion factors

to / from	Å	mm	cm	in	ft	yd	m	km	mile (imperial)
1 ångström (Å)	1.0	1.0×10^{-7}	1.0×10^{-8}	3.937×10^{-9}	3.2808×10^{-10}	1.0936×10^{-10}	1.0×10^{-10}	1.0×10^{-13}	6.2137×10^{-14}
1 millimeter (mm)	1.0×10^{7}	1.0	0.1	0.039 37	3.2808×10^{-3}	1.0936×10^{-3}	1.0×10^{-3}	1.0×10^{-6}	6.2137×10^{-7}
1 centimeter (cm)	1.0×10^{8}	10.0	1.0	0.393 70	0.032 808	0.010 936	0.01	1.0×10^{-5}	6.2137×10^{-6}
1 inch (in)	2.54×10^{8}	25.4	2.54	1.0	0.083 333	0.027 777	0.0254	2.54×10^{-5}	$1.578\,28 \times 10^{-5}$
1 foot (ft)	3.048×10^{9}	304.8	30.48	12.0	1.0	0.333 333	0.3048	3.048×10^{-4}	$1.893\,94 \times 10^{-4}$
1 yard (yd)	9.144×10^{9}	914.4	91.44	36.0	3.0	1.0	0.9144	9.144×10^{-4}	5.6818×10^{-4}
1 meter (m)	1.0×10^{10}	1.0×10^{3}	100.0	39.370 08	3.280 84	1.093 613	1.0	1.0×10^{-3}	$6.213\,71 \times 10^{-4}$
1 kilometer (km)	1.0×10^{13}	1.0×10^{6}	1.0×10^{5}	$3.937\,008 \times 10^{4}$	$3.280\,84 \times 10^{3}$	$1.093\,613 \times 10^{3}$	1.0×10^{3}	1.0	0.621 371
1 mile (imperial)	$1.609\,34 \times 10^{13}$	$1.609\,34 \times 10^{6}$	$1.609\,34 \times 10^{5}$	6.336×10^{4}	5.280×10^{3}	1.760×10^{3}	$1.609\,34 \times 10^{3}$	1.609 34	1.0

Table 2.2a. Miscellaneous units of area

Unit	m^2
1 acre	
UK	$4.046\,856\,4 \times 10^{3}$
US	$4.046\,856\,4 \times 10^{3}$
1 are(a)	100.0
1 barn	1.0×10^{-28}
1 barony	$1.618\,742\,56 \times 10^{7}$
1 centare	1.0
1 circular inch	$5.067\,07 \times 10^{-4}$
1 circular mile (or mil)	$5.067\,07 \times 10^{-10}$
1 circular millimeter	$0.785\,398 \times 10^{-6}$
1 Gunter's square chain (surveyor's)	404.6856
1 Gunter's square link (surveyor's)	0.040 468 56
1 hectare (ha)	1.0×10^{4}
1 hide	$4.046\,856\,4 \times 10^{5}$
1 load	55.7418
1 mil	$5.067\,07 \times 10^{-10}$
1 open window unit (owu)	0.092 903 04
1 Ramden's square chain (engineer's)	929.03
1 Ramden's square link (engineer's)	0.92 903
1 rood (imperial)	$1.011\,714\,106 \times 10^{3}$
1 section	$2.589\,99 \times 10^{6}$
1 shed	1.0×10^{-52}
1 square centimeter (cm^2)	1.0×10^{-4}
1 square decimeter (dm^2)	1.0×10^{-2}
1 square dekameter (Dm^2)	100.0
1 square fathom	3.344 508
1 square foot	
imperial	0.092 903
US survey	0.092 903 41
1 square hectometer (hm^2)	1.0×10^{4}
1 square inch (in^2)	6.4516×10^{-4}
1 square kilometer (km^2)	1.0×10^{6}
1 square meter (m^2)	1.0
1 square mile ($mile^2$)	$2.589\,99 \times 10^{6}$
1 square millimeter (mm^2)	1.0×10^{-6}
1 square of flooring	9.290 30
1 square perch (or square rod or square pole)	25.292 852 6
1 square pole (or square rod or square perch)	25.292 852 6
1 square rod (or square perch or square pole)	25.292 852 6
1 square yard (yd^2)	0.836 127 36
1 ton	5.574 18
1 township (US)	$9.323\,96 \times 10^{7}$
1 yard of land	$1.214\,056\,9 \times 10^{5}$

Table 2.2b. Area interconversion factors

from \ to	mm^2	cm^2	in^2	ft^2	yd^2	m^2	acre	hectare	$mile^2$
1 square millimeter (mm^2)	1.0	0.01	1.5500×10^{-3}	$1.076\,39 \times 10^{-5}$	$1.195\,99 \times 10^{-6}$	1.0×10^{-6}	$2.471\,05 \times 10^{-10}$	1.0×10^{-10}	$3.861\,02 \times 10^{-13}$
1 square centimeter (cm^2)	100.0	1.0	0.155 00	$1.076\,39 \times 10^{-3}$	$1.195\,99 \times 10^{-4}$	1.0×10^{-4}	$2.471\,05 \times 10^{-8}$	1.0×10^{-8}	$3.861\,02 \times 10^{-11}$
1 square inch (in^2)	645.16	6.4516	1.0	$6.944\,44 \times 10^{-3}$	$7.716\,05 \times 10^{-4}$	6.4516×10^{-4}	1.5942×10^{-7}	6.4516×10^{-8}	$2.490\,977 \times 10^{-10}$
1 square foot (ft^2)	9.2903×10^{4}	929.03	144.0	1.0	0.111 111	0.092 903	2.2957×10^{-5}	9.2903×10^{-6}	$3.587\,006 \times 10^{-8}$
1 square yard (yd^2)	$8.361\,27 \times 10^{5}$	$8.361\,27 \times 10^{3}$	1.296×10^{3}	9.0	1.0	0.836 127	2.0661×10^{-4}	$8.361\,27 \times 10^{-5}$	$3.228\,31 \times 10^{-7}$
1 square meter (m^2)	1.0×10^{6}	1.0×10^{4}	1.5500×10^{3}	10.763 91	1.195 99	1.0	$2.471\,05 \times 10^{-4}$	1.0×10^{-4}	$3.861\,02 \times 10^{-7}$
1 acre	$4.046\,86 \times 10^{9}$	$4.046\,86 \times 10^{7}$	$6.272\,64 \times 10^{6}$	4.3560×10^{4}	4.840×10^{3}	$4.046\,86 \times 10^{3}$	1.0	0.404 686	1.5625×10^{-3}
1 hectare	1.0×10^{10}	1.0×10^{8}	1.5500×10^{7}	$1.076\,39 \times 10^{5}$	$1.195\,99 \times 10^{4}$	1.0×10^{4}	2.471 05	1.0	$3.861\,02 \times 10^{-3}$
1 square mile ($mile^2$)	$2.589\,99 \times 10^{12}$	$2.589\,99 \times 10^{10}$	$4.014\,49 \times 10^{9}$	$2.787\,84 \times 10^{7}$	3.0976×10^{6}	$2.589\,99 \times 10^{6}$	640.0	258.999	1.0

Table 2.3a. Miscellaneous units of volume

Unit	m^3
1 acre-foot	$1.233\,481\,9 \times 10^3$
1 acre-inch	102.789 984
1 amagat (volume)	0.022 413 6
1 anker	0.037 873 48
1 aum	0.136 382 7
1 bag (UK)	0.109 106 1
1 barrel bulk	0.141 584
1 barrel	
ale, beer	0.136 344 5
herring	0.145 474 88
tar	0.120 471 38
UK	0.163 659 1
US, dry	0.115 627 12
US, liquid	0.119 240 446
US, petroleum	0.158 987 3
1 barrique	0.2250
1 base box	20.232 217
1 board foot	$2.359\,74 \times 10^{-3}$
1 bodge	$2.273\,045 \times 10^{-3}$
1 bucket (UK)	0.018 184 36
1 bushel	
UK	0.036 368 7
US	0.035 239 1
1 butt	
ale, beer	0.490 977 8
UK	0.476 961 9
wine	0.954 411 7
1 centiliter (cl)	1.0×10^{-5}
1 chaldron	
UK	1.309 27
US	1.268 606 5
1 chest	0.568 261 4
1 circular mil-foot	$1.544\,452 \times 10^{-10}$
1 comb (or coomb)	0.145 474 8
1 coomb (or comb)	0.145 474 8
1 cord	3.624 573 4
1 cord-foot	0.453 068 8
1 cran(e)	0.170 478 4
1 cubic centimeter (cm^3)	1.0×10^{-6}
1 cubic decimeter (dm^3)	1.0×10^{-3}
1 cubic dekameter (Dm^3)	1.0×10^3
1 cubic foot (ft^3)	
UK	0.028 316 8
US	0.028 317 016
1 cubic hectometer	1.0×10^6
1 cubic inch (in^3)	
UK	$1.638\,71 \times 10^{-5}$
US	$1.638\,716\,2 \times 10^{-5}$
1 cubic kilometer (km^3)	1.0×10^9
1 cubic meter (m^3)	1.0
1 cubic millimeter (mm^3)	1.0×10^{-9}
1 cubic yard (yd^3)	
UK	0.764 555
US	0.764 555
1 cup	$2.365\,882\,36 \times 10^{-4}$
1 decastere	10.0
1 deciliter (dl)	1.0×10^{-4}
1 decistere	0.1
1 dekaliter (dal)	0.01
1 drachm (UK, fluid)	$3.551\,63 \times 10^{-6}$
1 dram (US, fluid) (or liquid dram)	$3.696\,69 \times 10^{-6}$

Table 2.3a (contd)

Unit	m^3
1 fathom (cubic)	6.116 428 8
1 Festmeter (or Raummeter) (Fm)	1.0
1 firkin	
UK, ale or beer	0.040 914 819
US, ale or beer	0.037 097 027
1 gallon (gal)	
UK or imperial	$4.546\,091 \times 10^{-3}$
US, dry	$4.404\,883\,77 \times 10^{-3}$
US, liquid	$3.785\,411 \times 10^{-3}$
1 gallon, barn	
UK, milk	$9.092\,183 \times 10^{-3}$
US, milk	$9.084\,986\,4 \times 10^{-3}$
1 gill (gi)	
UK	$1.420\,65 \times 10^{-4}$
US	$1.182\,941 \times 10^{-4}$
1 hectoliter (hl)	0.1
1 hogshead	
ale, beer	0.245 488 91
honey, oil, spirits, vinegar, wine	0.238 602 92
pilchards	0.181 843 64
UK	0.2864
US	0.238 481
1 jar	0.113 652 275
1 kanne	1.0×10^{-3}
1 kilderkin (UK)	0.081 829 64
1 kiloliter	1.0
1 lambda (λ)	1.0×10^{-9}
1 last	2.909 496
1 liter (l) (here 1 liter = 1 dm^3)	1.0×10^{-3}
1 liquid dram (US)	$3.696\,69 \times 10^{-6}$
1 liquid ounce (US)	$2.957\,35 \times 10^{-5}$
1 load (or wey)	1.454 748
timber	1.415 84
unhewen timber	1.132 672
1 microliter (μl)	1.0×10^{-9}
1 mil (or milliliter) (ml)	1.0×10^{-6}
1 milliliter (or mil)	1.0×10^{-6}
1 minim	
UK	$5.919\,39 \times 10^{-8}$
US	$6.161\,15 \times 10^{-8}$
1 Mohr cubic centimeter	$1.000\,13 \times 10^{-6}$
1 noggin	$1.420\,652\,5 \times 10^{-4}$
1 ounce (fl oz)	
UK, fluid	$2.841\,31 \times 10^{-5}$
US, fluid (or liquid ounce)	$2.957\,35 \times 10^{-5}$
1 peck (pk)	
UK	$9.092\,18 \times 10^{-3}$
US	$8.809\,76 \times 10^{-3}$
1 perche (masonry)	0.700 840 8
1 pin	0.020 457 409
1 pint (pt)	
UK or imperial	$5.682\,61 \times 10^{-4}$
US, dry	5.5061×10^{-4}
US, liquid	$4.731\,765 \times 10^{-4}$
1 pipe	0.477 205 85
1 pottle	$2.273\,044 \times 10^{-3}$
1 puncheon	
ale, beer	0.327 318 55
honey, oil, spirits, winegar, wine	0.318 137 23

Table 2.3a (contd)

Unit	m^3
1 quart (qt)	
UK	$1.136\ 52 \times 10^{-3}$
US, dry	$1.101\ 221 \times 10^{-3}$
US, liquid	$9.463\ 53 \times 10^{-4}$
1 quart, reputed	$6.312\ 246\ 6 \times 10^{-4}$
1 quarter	0.290 95
1 quartern	
UK, dry	$2.273\ 044 \times 10^{-3}$
UK, liquid	$1.420\ 652 \times 10^{-4}$
1 Raummeter (Festmeter) (Rm)	1.0
1 rod (UK, volume)	28.316 847
1 run(d)let	0.068 172 264
1 sack	
coke	0.109 106 1
flour, salt	0.181 843 5
1 scruple (UK, fluid)	$1.183\ 878 \times 10^{-6}$
1 seam	0.290 949 6
1 stack	3.058 214 4
1 standard	
Petrograd	4.672 28
UK, timber	0.471 946 7
US, timber	4.672 272
1 standard volume of 1 mole perfect gas at 0°C, 1 atm	0.022 413 6
1 stere (French) (st)	1.0
1 strike (UK)	0.072 737
1 tablespoon	$1.478\ 676 \times 10^{-5}$
1 teaspoon	$4.928\ 92 \times 10^{-6}$
1 tierce	0.159 068 62
1 ton	
oil	8.046 581 07
sea freight	1.132 672
timber	1.415 84
1 ton register (internal capacity of ships)	2.831 684 6
1 trug	0.024 245 8
1 tun	
oil	0.954 679 11
honey, oil, spirits, vinegar, wine	0.954 411 696
1 wey (or load)	1.454 748
1 winchester quart	2.500×10^{-3}
1 winchester wine gallon (WWG)	$3.787\ 348 \times 10^{-3}$

Table 2.3b. Volume interconversion factors[a]

from \ to	cm^3	ml	in^3	l	ft^3	yd^3	m^3	pt	gal (US)
1 cubic centimeter (cm^3)	1.0	0.999 972	0.061 023 7	$9.999\,72 \times 10^{-4}$	$3.531\,47 \times 10^{-5}$	$1.307\,95 \times 10^{-6}$	1.0×10^{-6}	$2.113\,38 \times 10^{-3}$	2.6417×10^{-4}
1 milliliter (ml)	1.000 028	1.0	0.061 025 4	1.0×10^{-3}	$3.531\,57 \times 10^{-5}$	$1.307\,99 \times 10^{-6}$	$1.000\,028 \times 10^{-6}$	2.1134×10^{-3}	2.6418×10^{-4}
1 cubic inch (in^3)	16.387 06	16.3866	1.0	0.016 387	$5.787\,04 \times 10^{-4}$	$2.143\,35 \times 10^{-5}$	$1.638\,706 \times 10^{-5}$	0.034 632	4.329×10^{-3}
1 liter (l)	$1.000\,028 \times 10^{3}$	1.0×10^{3}	61.025 45	1.0	0.035 315 7	$1.307\,99 \times 10^{-3}$	$1.000\,028 \times 10^{-3}$	2.113 44	0.264 179
1 cubic foot (ft^3)	$2.831\,685 \times 10^{4}$	$2.831\,605 \times 10^{4}$	1.728×10^{3}	28.316 05	1.0	0.037 037	0.028 316 9	59.844 16	7.480 519
1 cubic yard (yd^3)	$7.645\,55 \times 10^{5}$	$7.645\,335 \times 10^{5}$	4.6656×10^{4}	764.5335	27.0	1.0	0.764 555	$1.615\,79 \times 10^{3}$	201.97
1 cubic meter (m^3)	1.0×10^{6}	$9.999\,72 \times 10^{5}$	$6.102\,37 \times 10^{4}$	999.972	35.314 67	1.307 951	1.0	$2.113\,38 \times 10^{3}$	264.172
1 pint (pt)	473.176	473.163	28.875	0.473 163 2	0.016 71	6.1889×10^{-4}	$4.731\,76 \times 10^{-4}$	1.0	0.125
1 gallon (gal (US))	$3.785\,412 \times 10^{3}$	$3.785\,31 \times 10^{3}$	231.0	3.785 306	0.133 681	$4.951\,13 \times 10^{-3}$	$3.785\,41 \times 10^{-3}$	8.0	1.0

[a] In this table the definitions of milliliter (ml) and liter (l) refer to the convention adopted before 1964, that is 1 liter (1901) = 1.000 028 dm^3.

2.4 Angle (plane and solid) (rad and sr)

According to the definition, the angle is between two radii of a circle that cut off on the circumference an arc equal in length to the radius. The radian is the coherent SI unit of plane angle. It is a supplementary unit. The steradin is the coherent SI unit of solid angle. It is also a supplementary unit.

The miscellaneous units and the conversion factors to radian are listed in Table 2.4a. Table 2.4b lists the units of solid angle. The interconversion factors for the various units of angular (plane) measure are tabulated in Table 2.4c.

Table 2.4a. Miscellaneous units of plane angles

Unit	rad
1 angular mil	1.0×10^{-3}
1 arcmin	$2.908\,88 \times 10^{-4}$
1 centesimal minute	$1.570\,796\,3 \times 10^{-4}$
1 centesimal second	$1.570\,796\,3 \times 10^{-6}$
1 centrad	0.01
1 circle (or circumference)	6.283 185 3
1 circumference (or circle)	6.283 185 3
1 degree (angular)	0.017 453 3
1 gon (or grade)	0.015 708
1 grade (or gon)	0.015 708
1 minute (angular)	$2.908\,88 \times 10^{-4}$
1 octant	0.785 398 16
1 quadrant	1.570 796 33
1 rad	1.0
1 revolution	6.283 185 3
1 right angle	1.570 80
1 second (angular)	$4.848\,14 \times 10^{-6}$
1 sextant	1.047 197 551
1 sign	0.523 598 775
1 turn	6.283 185 31

Table 2.4b. Miscellaneous units of solid angles

Unit	sr
1 degree, square (or square degree)	$3.046\,174 \times 10^{-4}$
1 hemisphere	6.283 185 3
1 space (entire)	12.566 370 4
1 sphere (or solid angle)	12.566 370 4
1 spherical right angle	1.570 796 3
1 square degree	$3.046\,174 \times 10^{-4}$
1 steradian (sr)	1.0

Table 2.4c. Plain angle interconversion factors

from \ to	s	min	grade	degree	rad	quadrant	circle
1 second (s)	1.0	0.016 666 7	$3.086\,42 \times 10^{-4}$	$2.777\,78 \times 10^{-4}$	$4.848\,14 \times 10^{-6}$	$3.086\,42 \times 10^{-6}$	$7.716\,049 \times 10^{-7}$
1 minute (min)	60.0	1.0	0.018 518 5	0.016 666 7	$2.908\,88 \times 10^{-4}$	$1.851\,852 \times 10^{-4}$	4.6293×10^{-5}
1 grade	3.24×10^{3}	54.0	1.0	0.9	0.015 708	0.01	2.5×10^{-3}
1 degree	3.6×10^{3}	60.0	1.111 111	1.0	0.017 453 3	0.011 111 1	$2.777\,778 \times 10^{-3}$
1 radian (rad)	$2.062\,648 \times 10^{5}$	$3.437\,75 \times 10^{3}$	63.661 98	57.295 78	1.0	0.636 619 8	0.159 154 9
1 quadrant	3.24×10^{5}	5.4×10^{3}	100.0	90.0	1.570 796	1.0	0.25
1 circle	1.296×10^{6}	2.16×10^{4}	400.0	360.0	6.283 185	4.0	1.0

2.5 Time (s)

The second is defined as the duration of 9 192 631 770 periods of the radiation corresponding to the transition between the two hyperfine levels of the ground state of the cesium-133 atom.

The miscellaneous units of time and the conversion factors to second are listed in Table 2.5a. The interconversion factors for the various units of time are given in Table 2.5b.

Table 2.5a. Miscellaneous units of time

Unit	s
1 aeon	3.1536×10^{16}
1 blink	0.864
1 cé	864.0
1 cron	3.156×10^{13}
1 day (d)	
mean solar	8.6400×10^{4}
sideral	8.6164×10^{4}
1 degree of time	864.0
1 hour (h)	
mean solar	3.600×10^{3}
sideral	$3.590\,170\,4 \times 10^{3}$
1 microsecond (μs)	1.0×10^{-6}
1 millisecond (ms)	1.0×10^{-3}
1 minute (min)	
mean solar	60.0
sideral	59.836 174
1 month (mth)	
mean calendral	2.628×10^{6}
30 days	2.5920×10^{6}
31 days	2.6784×10^{6}
1 nanosecond (ns)	1.0×10^{-9}
1 second (s)	
mean solar	1.0
sideral	0.997 269 56
1 shake	1.0×10^{-8}
1 week (wk)	$6.048\,00 \times 10^{5}$
1 year (yr)	
sideral	$3.155\,815 \times 10^{7}$
tropical or mean solar	$3.155\,692\,6 \times 10^{7}$
365 days or calendral year	3.1536×10^{7}

Table 2.5b. Time interconversion factors

from \ to	s	min	h	d	wk	30-d mth	31-d mth	yr
1 second (s)	1.0	0.016 666 67	$2.777\,778 \times 10^{-4}$	$1.157\,41 \times 10^{-5}$	$1.653\,44 \times 10^{-6}$	$3.858\,02 \times 10^{-7}$	$3.733\,572 \times 10^{-7}$	$3.170\,979 \times 10^{-8}$
1 minute (min)	60.0	1.0	0.016 666 67	$6.944\,44 \times 10^{-4}$	$9.920\,63 \times 10^{-5}$	$2.314\,82 \times 10^{-5}$	$2.240\,143 \times 10^{-5}$	$1.902\,588 \times 10^{-6}$
1 hour (h)	3.6×10^{3}	60.0	1.0	0.041 666 7	$5.952\,38 \times 10^{-3}$	$1.388\,89 \times 10^{-3}$	$1.344\,086 \times 10^{-3}$	$1.141\,553 \times 10^{-4}$
1 day (d)	8.64×10^{4}	1.44×10^{3}	24.0	1.0	0.142 857 1	0.033 333 3	0.032 258 06	$2.739\,726 \times 10^{-3}$
1 week (wk)	6.048×10^{5}	1.008×10^{4}	168.0	7.0	1.0	0.233 333 3	0.225 806 5	0.019 178 08
1 month, 30 days (30-d mth)	2.592×10^{6}	4.32×10^{4}	720.0	30.0	4.285 714	1.0	0.967 741 9	0.082 191 78
1 month, 31 days (31-d mth)	2.6784×10^{6}	4.464×10^{4}	744.0	31.0	4.428 571	1.033 333 3	1.0	0.084 931 51
1 year, 365 days (yr)	3.1536×10^{7}	5.256×10^{5}	8.76×10^{3}	365.0	52.142 86	12.166 678	11.774 194	1.0

2.6 Velocity (linear) ($m\ s^{-1}$)

The ratio between the length and time is known as velocity. Units of length given in Table 2.1a may be used in combination with the units of time, given in Table 2.5a, for expressing linear velocity or speed.

The traditional units of velocity and their conversion factors to the SI unit of meter per second are given in Table 2.6a. Interconversion factors for the units of linear velocity are listed in Table 2.6b.

Table 2.6a. Miscellaneous units of linear velocity

Unit	$m\ s^{-1}$
1 benz	1.0
1 centimeter per hour ($cm\ h^{-1}$)	$2.777\,78 \times 10^{-6}$
1 centimeter per minute ($cm\ min^{-1}$)	$1.666\,67 \times 10^{-4}$
1 centimeter per second ($cm\ s^{-1}$)	0.01
1 centimeter per year ($cm\ yr^{-1}$)	$3.170\,979 \times 10^{-10}$
1 foot per hour ($ft\ h^{-1}$)	8.4667×10^{-5}
1 foot per minute ($ft\ min^{-1}$)	5.08×10^{-3}
1 foot per second ($ft\ s^{-1}$)	0.3048
1 inch per hour ($in\ h^{-1}$)	$7.055\,556 \times 10^{-6}$
1 inch per minute ($in\ min^{-1}$)	$4.233\,33 \times 10^{-4}$
1 inch per second ($in\ s^{-1}$)	0.0254
1 kilometer per hour ($km\ h^{-1}$)	0.277 778
1 kilometer per minute ($km\ min^{-1}$)	16.666 67
1 kilometer per second ($km\ s^{-1}$)	1.0×10^{3}
1 kine	0.01
1 knot (kn)	
international	0.514 444
UK	0.514 773
1 meter per hour ($m\ h^{-1}$)	$2.777\,78 \times 10^{-4}$
1 meter per minute ($m\ min^{-1}$)	0.016 666 7
1 meter per second ($m\ s^{-1}$)	1.0
1 mile per hour	0.447 04
1 mile per minute	26.8224
1 mile per second	$1.609\,344 \times 10^{3}$
1 yard per hour ($yd\ h^{-1}$)	2.5400×10^{-4}
1 yard per minute ($yd\ min^{-1}$)	0.015 24
1 yard per second ($yd\ s^{-1}$)	0.9144

Table 2.6b. Velocity (linear) interconversion factors

from \ to	ft min^{-1}	cm s^{-1}	m min^{-1}	km h^{-1}	ft s^{-1}	mile h^{-1}	kn	m s^{-1}	km min^{-1}
1 foot per minute (ft min^{-1})	1.0	0.508	0.3048	0.018 288	0.016 666 67	0.011 363 6	9.8747×10^{-3}	5.08×10^{-3}	3.048×10^{-4}
1 centimeter per second (cm s^{-1})	1.968 504	1.0	0.6	0.036	0.032 808 4	0.022 369 4	0.019 438	0.01	6.0×10^{-4}
1 meter per minute (m min^{-1})	3.280 84	1.666 666 7	1.0	0.06	0.054 680 7	0.037 282 3	0.032 397 4	0.016 666 7	1.0×10^{-3}
1 kilometer per hour (km h^{-1})	54.680 66	27.777 778	16.666 667	1.0	0.911 344 4	0.621 371 2	0.539 956 8	0.277 777 8	-0.016 666 7
1 foot per second (ft s^{-1})	60.0	30.48	18.288	1.097 28	1.0	0.681 818 2	0.592 483 8	0.3048	0.018 288
1 mile per hour (mile h^{-1})	88.0	44.704	26.8224	1.609 344	1.466 667	1.0	0.868 976 2	0.447 04	0.026 822 4
1 knot (kn)	101.2686	51.444 44	30.866 667	1.852	1.687 81	1.150 779	1.0	0.514 444	0.030 866 67
1 meter per second (m s^{-1})	196.8504	100.0	60.0	3.6	3.280 84	2.236 936	1.943 844	1.0	0.06
1 kilometer per minute (km min^{-1})	$3.280 84 \times 10^{3}$	$1.666 667 \times 10^{3}$	1.0×10^{3}	60.0	54.680 66	37.282 27	32.397 41	16.666 667	1.0

2.7 Velocity (angular) or frequency (Hz)

The angular velocity is defined as the reciprocal of periodic time, or the number of periodic motions completed in unit time. The angular velocity or frequency is the ratio between the angle (expressed in radian, revolution or degree) and the time.

The following alternative terms are often used instead of angular velocity:

speed of rotation
rotational velocity
rotational speed
rotational frequency (frequency)

The commonly used units of angular velocity are listed in Table 2.7a. The various interconversion factors for angular velocity units are compiled in Table 2.7b.

Table 2.7a. Miscellaneous units of angular velocity (frequency)

Unit	Hz
1 cycle per second (or revolution per second)	1.0
1 degree per hour (degree h^{-1})	$7.716\,047\,2 \times 10^{-7}$
1 degree per minute (degree min^{-1})	$4.629\,629 \times 10^{-5}$
1 degree per second (degree s^{-1})	$2.777\,78 \times 10^{-3}$
1 hertz (Hz)	1.0
1 radian per hour (rad h^{-1})	$4.420\,970\,5 \times 10^{-5}$
1 radian per minute (rad min^{-1})	$2.652\,582 \times 10^{-3}$
1 radian per second (rad s^{-1})	0.159 154 94
1 revolution per hour (rev h^{-1})	$2.777\,78 \times 10^{-4}$
1 revolution per minute (rev min^{-1})	0.016 667
1 revolution per second (or cycle per second) (rev s^{-1})	1.0

Table 2.7b. Angular velocity (frequency) interconversion factors

from \ to	Hz	rev min^{-1}	degree s^{-1}	rad s^{-1}	degree min^{-1}	rad min^{-1}
1 revolution per second (hertz (Hz))	1.0	60.0	360.0	6.283 19	2.1600×10^{4}	376.991
1 revolution per minute (rev min^{-1})	0.016 667	1.0	6.0	0.104 720	360.0	6.283 19
1 degree per second (degree s^{-1})	$2.777\,78 \times 10^{-3}$	0.166 667	1.0	0.017 453 3	60.0	1.047 20
1 radian per second (rad s^{-1})	0.159 154 94	9.549 296 6	57.295 779	1.0	$3.437\,747 \times 10^{3}$	60.0
1 degree per minute (degree min^{-1})	$4.629\,629 \times 10^{-5}$	$2.777\,78 \times 10^{-3}$	0.016 666 7	$2.908\,88 \times 10^{-4}$	1.0	0.017 453 3
1 radian per minute (rad min^{-1})	$2.652\,58 \times 10^{-3}$	0.159 155	0.954 930	0.016 666 7	57.2958	1.0

2.8 Acceleration (m s^{-2})

Acceleration is expressed as the ratio between units of length and the time squared.

There are several units of acceleration (*see* Table 2.8a). The various interconversion factors for the units are given in Table 2.8b.

Table 2.8a. Miscellaneous units of acceleration

Unit	m s^{-2}
1 celo	0.3048
1 centimeter per square second (cm s^{-2})	0.01
1 foot per square second (ft s^{-2})	0.3048
1 fors (f)	9.806 65
1 G (gravity)	9.806 65
1 Galileo (Gal)	0.010
1 grav or gravity (G)	9.806 65
1 kilometer per hour per second (km h^{-1} s^{-1})	0.277 778
1 leo	10.0
1 meter per square second (m s^{-2})	1.0
1 mile per hour per minute (mile h^{-1} min^{-1})	$7.450\ 666 \times 10^{-3}$
1 mile per hour per second (mile h^{-1} s^{-1})	0.447 040
1 milligal (mGal)	1.0×10^{-5}

Table 2.8b. Acceleration interconversion factors

from \ to	mGal	cm s^{-2}	m s^{-2}	ft s^{-2}	G
1 milligal (mGal)	1.0	1.0×10^{-3}	1.0×10^{-5}	$3.280\ 84 \times 10^{-5}$	$1.019\ 72 \times 10^{-6}$
1 centimeter per square second (cm s^{-2})	1.0×10^{3}	1.0	0.01	0.032 808 4	$1.019\ 72 \times 10^{-3}$
1 meter per square second (m s^{-2})	1.0×10^{5}	100.0	1.0	3.280 84	0.101 972
1 foot per square second (ft s^{-2})	3.048×10^{4}	30.48	0.3048	1.0	0.031 081
1 standard acceleration due to gravity (G)	$9.806\ 65 \times 10^{5}$	980.665	9.806 65	32.1740	1.0

2.9 Mass (kg)

The kilogram is the unit of mass. It is equal to the mass of the international prototype of the kilogram, which is kept in Sèvres near Paris by the Bureau International des Poids et Mesures.

The units of mass may be expressed in various systems (e.g., metric, SI, imperial, USA, apothecaries, troy, etc.). Table 2.9a presents these units in alphabetical order; their relationships to the SI unit are given. The interconversion factors for the common units of mass are tabulated in Table 2.9b.

Table 2.9a. Miscellaneous units of mass

Unit	kg
1 assay ton	
UK	0.032 667
US	0.029 166 7
1 atomic mass unit, international (or dalton)	$1.660\,24 \times 10^{-27}$
1 atomic unit of mass	9.1084×10^{-31}
1 atomic weight unit	
chemical mass unit	$1.660\,24 \times 10^{-27}$
physical mass unit	$1.659\,79 \times 10^{-27}$
1 avogram	$1.660\,36 \times 10^{-27}$
1 bag (cement, US)	42.637 682 8
1 bale (cinnamon)	41.957 294 2
1 barge (coal)	$2.154\,019\,45 \times 10^{4}$
1 barrel (candles, potash, potatoes)	54.431 084 4
1 bes	1.0×10^{-3}
1 boll (flour)	63.502 931 8
1 bottle (mercury)	39.008 944
1 brieze	1.0×10^{-3}
1 bushel (wheat)	27.215 542
1 carat	
metric	2.0×10^{-4}
1877	2.053×10^{-4}
troy	$2.591\,956 \times 10^{-4}$
1 cask (soda)	177.808 207
1 central (or quintal or short or new hundredweight)	45.359 237
1 centigram	1.0×10^{-5}
1 centner (or central or quintal or short hundredweight)	45.359 237
1 chaldron (coal)	$1.295\,459\,8 \times 10^{3}$
1 chemical mass unit (or atomic mass unit)	$1.660\,24 \times 10^{-27}$
1 chest (tea)	49.895 161
1 clove (British stones)	3.6287
1 crith	8.9885×10^{-5}
1 cubic foot	
common brick	54.431 084 4
water (60°F)	28.290 556 1
1 cubic yard (sand)	$1.224\,699\,4 \times 10^{3}$
1 dalton (or international atomic mass unit)	$1.660\,24 \times 10^{-27}$
1 decigram (dg)	1.0×10^{-4}
1 dekagram (dag)	0.01
1 drachm (apothecaries)	$3.887\,93 \times 10^{-3}$
1 dram	
UK or avoirdupois	$1.771\,85 \times 10^{-3}$
US or apothecaries or troy	$3.887\,93 \times 10^{-3}$
1 drop (spirits)	$1.771\,843\,7 \times 10^{-3}$
1 dyn (or dyne)	$1.019\,716 \times 10^{-6}$
1 electron volt	$1.782\,53 \times 10^{-36}$
1 fag(g)ot (steel)	54.431 084 4
1 firkin (soap)	29.029 912
1 flask (mercury, US)	34.019 427 75
1 fodder (lead)	$1.088\,621\,688 \times 10^{3}$
1 fother (lead, etc.)	990.645 736
1 fotmal (lead, etc.)	31.751 465 9
1 gamma (or microgram) (γ or μg)	1.0×10^{-9}

Table 2.9a (contd)

Unit	kg
1 gee pound (or slug)	14.593 881
1 glug	0.980 665
1 grain	
imperial	$6.479\,891 \times 10^{-5}$
metric	5.0×10^{-5}
1 gram (or gramme) (g)	1.0×10^{-3}
1 grave	$1.000\,028 \times 10^{-3}$
1 gross ton (or long ton)	$1.016\,046\,909 \times 10^{3}$
1 hectogram (hg)	0.1
1 hundredweight (cwt)	
avoirdupois or long	50.802 345
long or long quintal	50.802 345
short or short or new quintal or central	45.359 237
troy	37.324 172
1 hyl (or mug or metric slug or par)	9.806 65
1 international corn bushel	27.2155
1 joule per centimeter ($J\,cm^{-1}$)	10.2000
1 joule per meter ($J\,m^{-1}$)	0.102 000
1 keel (coal)	$2.154\,019\,45 \times 10^{4}$
1 keg (nails, US)	45.359 237
1 kilogram (kg)	1.0
1 kip	453.592 37
1 last (gunpowder)	$1.088\,621\,688 \times 10^{3}$
1 livre	0.50
1 long hundredweight (or long quintal)	50.802 345 4
1 long quarter (US)	254.011 727 2
1 long ton (or gross ton)	$1.016\,046\,909 \times 10^{3}$
1 mass of oxygen atom	$2.656\,384 \times 10^{-26}$
1 mast	0.933 105
1 matt (cloves)	36.287 389 6
1 megagram (Mg)	1.0×10^{3}
1 metric carat	2.0×10^{-4}
1 metric slug (or hyl or mug or par)	9.806 65
1 metric ton	1.0×10^{3}
1 microgram (or gamma) (μg)	1.0×10^{-9}
1 millier (or tonne or tonneau or metric ton) (t)	1.0×10^{3}
1 milligram (mg)	1.0×10^{-6}
1 millimass unit	$1.037\,38 \times 10^{-31}$
1 mounce	0.0250
1 mug (or hyl or metric slug or par)	9.806 65
1 myriagram	10.0
1 nail (butter, cheese)	3.628 738 96
1 new hundredweight	45.359 237
1 newton	0.101 971 6
1 ounce (oz)	
avoirdupois	0.028 349 5
apothecaries	0.031 103 5
metric or metric ounce	0.025
troy	0.031 103 5
1 pack (wool)	108.862 168 8
1 par (or hyl or mug or metric slug)	9.806 65
1 peck (flour)	6.350 293 18
1 physical mass unit (or atomic mass unit)	$1.659\,79 \times 10^{-27}$
1 pocket (wool)	82.553 811 34
1 point	2.0×10^{-6}
1 pound (lb)	
avoirdupois	0.453 592 37
US troy or apothecaries	0.373 242
1 poundal	0.014 098 08

Table 2.9a (contd)

Unit	kg
1 quarter (qr)	
UK avoirdupois	12.700 586
troy	9.331 043 04
1 quintal	
imperial	45.359 237
metric (q)	100.0
1 room (coal)	$7.112\ 328\ 37 \times 10^3$
1 sack (salt, US)	97.522 359 5
1 scruple (apothecaries)	$1.295\ 98 \times 10^{-3}$
1 seam (glass)	54.431 084 4
1 shipload (coal)	$4.308\ 038\ 9 \times 10^5$
1 short assay ton	0.029 166 7
1 short hundredweight (or central or short quintal)	45.359 237
1 short quarter (or US avoirdupois or US short)	226.796 185
1 short ton (or net ton)	907.184 74
1 slug (or gee pound)	14.593 881
1 stathm	1.0×10^{-3}
1 stone (imperial)	6.350 293 18
1 tod (wool)	12.700 586 4
1 ton	
troy	746.483 443 2
UK avoirdupois or long ton (ton)	$1.016\ 046\ 91 \times 10^3$
1 tonne (or tonneau or metric ton or millier) (t)	1.0×10^3
1 tonneau (or tonne or metric ton or millier)	1.0×10^3
1 tother (lead)	$1.088\ 621\ 688 \times 10^3$
1 troy pennyweight	$1.555\ 174 \times 10^{-3}$
1 truss (straw)	16.329 325 3
1 tub (butter)	38.101 759 1
1 wey (UK mass)	114.305 277 2

Table 2.9b. Mass interconversion factors

from \ to	grain	g	dram	oz	lb	kg	short ton	long ton	t
1 grain	1.0	0.064 798 9	0.036 571	$2.285\,71 \times 10^{-3}$	$1.428\,57 \times 10^{-4}$	$6.479\,89 \times 10^{-5}$	$7.142\,86 \times 10^{-8}$	$6.377\,55 \times 10^{-8}$	$6.479\,89 \times 10^{-8}$
1 gram (g)	15.432 36	1.0	0.564 383 4	0.035 273 96	$2.204\,623 \times 10^{-3}$	1.0×10^{-3}	$1.102\,31 \times 10^{-6}$	$9.842\,07 \times 10^{-7}$	1.0×10^{-6}
1 dram	27.343 75	1.771 845	1.0	0.0625	$3.906\,25 \times 10^{-3}$	$1.771\,845 \times 10^{-3}$	1.9531×10^{-6}	$1.743\,86 \times 10^{-6}$	$1.771\,85 \times 10^{-6}$
1 ounce (oz)	437.5	28.349 523	16.0	1.0	0.0625	0.028 349 523	3.125×10^{-5}	$2.790\,18 \times 10^{-5}$	$2.834\,95 \times 10^{-5}$
1 pound (lb)	7.0×10^{3}	453.5924	256.0	16.0	1.0	0.453 592 4	5.0×10^{-4}	$4.464\,29 \times 10^{-4}$	$4.535\,92 \times 10^{-4}$
1 kilogram (kg)	$1.543\,24 \times 10^{4}$	1.0×10^{3}	564.38	35.273 96	2.204 623	1.0	$1.102\,31 \times 10^{-3}$	$9.842\,07 \times 10^{-4}$	1.0×10^{-3}
1 short ton	1.4×10^{7}	$9.071\,847 \times 10^{5}$	5.12×10^{5}	3.2×10^{4}	2.0×10^{3}	907.185	1.0	0.892 857 1	0.907 184 74
1 long ton	1.568×10^{7}	$1.016\,047 \times 10^{6}$	5.7344×10^{5}	3.584×10^{4}	2.24×10^{3}	$1.016\,047 \times 10^{3}$	1.12	1.0	1.016 047
1 metric ton (t)	1.5432×10^{7}	1.0×10^{6}	$5.643\,83 \times 10^{5}$	3.5274×10^{4}	$2.204\,62 \times 10^{3}$	1.0×10^{3}	1.102 311	0.984 207	1.0

2.10 Mass per unit length (line density) (kg m^{-1})

Mass per unit length is often called linear density. It is expressed as the ratio between the units of mass given in Table 2.9a and the units of length given in Table 2.1a.

The traditional units listed in Table 2.10a have been compiled from the technical literature (*see* References). The interconversion factors for the units of mass per unit length are given in Table 2.10b.

Table 2.10a. Miscellaneous units of mass per unit length

Unit	kg m^{-1}
1 denier (= 1 g/9 km)	$1.111\,12 \times 10^{-7}$
1 drex (= 1 g/10^4 m)	1.0×10^{-7}
1 dyne per centimeter (dyn cm^{-1})	$1.019\,716 \times 10^{-4}$
1 dyne per inch (dyn in^{-1})	$4.014\,630\,8 \times 10^{-5}$
1 gram per centimeter (g cm^{-1})	0.1
1 gram per foot (g ft^{-1})	$3.280\,846 \times 10^{-3}$
1 gram per inch (g in^{-1})	0.039 370 08
1 gram per kilometer (tex) (g km^{-1})	1.0×10^{-6}
1 gram per meter (g m^{-1})	1.0×10^{-3}
1 gram per millimeter (g mm^{-1})	1.0
1 kilogram per kilometer (kg km^{-1})	1.0×10^{-3}
1 kilogram per meter (kg m^{-1})	1.0
1 milligram per centimeter (mg cm^{-1})	1.0×10^{-4}
1 milligram per inch (mg in^{-1})	$3.937\,008 \times 10^{-5}$
1 milligram per millimeter (mg mm^{-1})	1.0×10^{-3}
1 ounce per centimeter (oz cm^{-1})	2.834 963 17
1 ounce per inch (oz in^{-1})	1.116 125
1 pli	17.8580
1 poumar	$4.960\,55 \times 10^{-7}$
1 pound per foot (lb ft^{-1})	1.488 16
1 pound per inch (lb in^{-1})	17.8580
1 pound per meter (lb m^{-1})	0.453 592 4
1 pound per mile (lb $mile^{-1}$)	$2.818\,49 \times 10^{-4}$
1 pound per yard (lb yd^{-1})	0.496 055
1 poundal per inch (pdl in^{-1})	0.555 043 7
1 tex (gram per kilometer, g km^{-1})	1.0×10^{-6}
1 ton (UK) per mile (ton $mile^{-1}$)	0.631 342
1 ton (UK) per 1000 yards	1.111 16
1 tonne (metric ton) per kilometer (t km^{-1})	1.0

Table 2.10b. Mass per unit length interconversion factors

from \ to	kg m^{-1}	ton mile^{-1}	lb yd^{-1}	lb ft^{-1}	lb in^{-1}	g cm^{-1}	oz in^{-1}	ton km^{-1}
1 kilogram per meter (kg m^{-1})	1.0	1.583 928	2.015 905	0.671 970	0.055 997 3	10.0	0.895 959	0.984 207
1 long ton per mile (ton mile^{-1})	0.631 342	1.0	1.272 727	0.424 242	0.035 353 5	6.313 439	0.565 657	0.621 373
1 pound per yard (lb yd^{-1})	0.496 055	0.785 714	1.0	0.333 333	0.027 777 8	4.960 542	0.444 444	0.488 220
1 pound per foot (lb ft^{-1})	1.488 16	2.357 145	3.0	1.0	0.083 333 3	14.881 627	1.333 333	1.464 661
1 pound per inch (lb in^{-1})	17.858	28.285 742	36.0	12.0	1.0	178.580	16.0	17.575 936
1 gram per centimeter (g cm^{-1})	0.1	0.158 392 8	0.201 590 8	0.067 196 9	$5.599\,73 \times 10^{-3}$	1.0	0.089 595 9	0.098 420 7
1 ounce per inch (oz in^{-1})	1.116 125	1.767 856	2.25	0.75	0.0625	11.161 22	1.0	1.098 496
1 long ton per kilometer (ton km^{-1})	1.016 05	1.609 349	2.048 387	0.682 796	0.056 899 6	10.160 46	0.910 336	1.0

2.11 Mass per unit area (area density or pressure) (kg m^{-2})

The mass per unit area is the ratio between the units of mass given in Table 2.9a and the units of area given in Table 2.2a.

The units of mass per unit area listed in Table 2.11a have been taken from the technical literature (*see* References). The various interconversion factors are presented in Table 2.11b.

Table 2.11a. Miscellaneous units of mass per unit area

Unit	kg m^{-2}
1 dyne per square centimeter (dyn cm^{-2})	0.010 197 162
1 gram per square centimeter (g cm^{-2})	10.0
1 gram per square meter (g m^{-2})	1.0×10^{-3}
1 kilogram per hectare (kg ha^{-1})	1.0×10^{-4}
1 kilogram per square centimeter (kg cm^{-2})	1.0×10^{4}
1 kilogram per square meter (kg m^{-2})	1.0
1 kilogram per square millimeter (kg mm^{-2})	1.0×10^{6}
1 milligram per square meter (mg m^{-2})	0.01
1 milligram per square millimeter (mg mm^{-2})	1.0
1 ounce per square foot (oz ft^{-2})	0.305 152
1 ounce per square inch (oz in^{-2})	43.941 849
1 ounce per square yard (oz yd^{-2})	0.033 905 7
1 pound per acre (lb acre^{-1})	$1.120\,85 \times 10^{-4}$
1 pound per square foot (lb ft^{-2})	4.882 427 6
1 pound per square inch (lb in^{-2})	703.069 595
1 pound per square yard (lb yd^{-2})	0.542 492
1 pound per thousand square feet (lb 1000ft^{-2})	$4.882\,43 \times 10^{-3}$
1 poundal per square inch (pdl in^{-2})	21.852 048 5
1 ton (long) per square foot	$1.093\,666 \times 10^{4}$
1 ton (long) per square inch	$1.574\,88 \times 10^{6}$
1 ton (long) per square mile	$3.922\,98 \times 10^{-4}$
1 ton (short) per square foot	$9.764\,855\,6 \times 10^{3}$
1 ton (short) per square inch	$1.406\,139\,2 \times 10^{6}$

Table 2.11b. Mass per unit area interconversion factors

from \ to	kg m^{-2}	ton $mile^{-2}$	lb yd^{-2}	lb ft^{-2}	lb in^{-2}	g cm^{-2}	oz in^{-2}	ton km^{-2}	ton $acre^{-1}$
1 kilogram per square meter (kg m^{-2})	1.0	$2.549\,082\,6 \times 10^{3}$	1.843 345	0.204 816	$1.422\,33 \times 10^{-3}$	0.1	0.022 757 4	984.206	3.982 937
1 long ton per square mile (ton $mile^{-2}$)	$3.922\,98 \times 10^{-4}$	1.0	$7.231\,41 \times 10^{-4}$	$8.034\,886 \times 10^{-5}$	$5.579\,783 \times 10^{-7}$	$3.922\,976 \times 10^{-5}$	$8.927\,657 \times 10^{-6}$	0.386 102 2	1.5625×10^{-3}
1 pound per square yard (lb yd^{-2})	0.542 492	$1.382\,856\,7 \times 10^{3}$	1.0	0.111 111 1	$7.716\,05 \times 10^{-4}$	0.054 249 18	0.012 345 68	533.924	2.160 714 2
1 pound per square foot (lb ft^{-2})	4.882 43	$1.244\,572\,8 \times 10^{4}$	9.0	1.0	$6.944\,44 \times 10^{-3}$	0.488 242	0.111 111	$4.805\,32 \times 10^{3}$	19.446 428
1 pound per square inch (lb in^{-2})	703.07	$1.792\,184\,3 \times 10^{6}$	$1.295\,999\,9 \times 10^{3}$	144.0	1.0	70.306 805	16.0	$6.919\,657 \times 10^{5}$	2.8003×10^{3}
1 gram per square centimeter (g cm^{-2})	10.0	$2.549\,082\,6 \times 10^{4}$	18.433 457	2.048 163 8	0.014 223 37	1.0	0.227 573	$9.842\,064 \times 10^{3}$	39.829 457
1 ounce per square inch (oz in^{-2})	43.941 849	$1.120\,115 \times 10^{5}$	80.999 994	9.0	0.0625	4.394 185	1.0	$4.324\,785 \times 10^{4}$	175.0207
1 long ton per square kilometer (ton km^{-2})	$1.016\,047 \times 10^{-3}$	2.589 988	$1.872\,925 \times 10^{-3}$	$2.081\,028 \times 10^{-4}$	$1.445\,158 \times 10^{-6}$	$1.016\,047 \times 10^{-4}$	$2.312\,253 \times 10^{-5}$	1.0	$4.046\,856 \times 10^{-3}$
1 long ton per acre (ton $acre^{-1}$)	0.251 071	640.0	0.462 81	0.051 423 32	$3.571\,064 \times 10^{-4}$	0.025 107 04	$5.713\,61 \times 10^{-3}$	247.1054	1.0

2.12 Area per unit mass (specific surface) ($m^2\ kg^{-1}$)

The ratio between the units of area given in Table 2.2a and the units of mass given in Table 2.9a is called specific surface or area per unit mass.

The various conversion factors of specific surface to $m^2\ kg^{-1}$ (SI unit) are presented in Table 2.12.

Table 2.12. Miscellaneous units of area per unit mass

Unit	$m^2\ kg^{-1}$
1 acre per pound (acre lb^{-1})	$8.921\,79 \times 10^3$
1 hectare per kilogram (ha kg^{-1})	1.0×10^4
1 square centimeter per milligram ($cm^2\ mg^{-1}$)	100.0
1 square foot per ounce ($ft^2\ oz^{-1}$)	3.277 06
1 square meter per gram ($m^2\ g^{-1}$)	1.0×10^3
1 square meter per kilogram ($m^2\ kg^{-1}$)	1.0
1 square mile per long ton ($mile^2\ ton^{-1}$)	$2.549\,08 \times 10^3$
1 square millimeter per milligram ($mm^2\ mg^{-1}$)	1.0
1 square yard per ounce ($yd^2\ oz^{-1}$)	29.4935
1 thousand square feet per pound (1000 $ft^2\ lb^{-1}$)	204.816

2.13 Area per unit volume (or capacity) ($m^2\ m^{-3}$)

The area per unit volume or area per unit capacity is the ratio between the units of area given in Table 2.2a and the units of volume given in Table 2.3a.

The conversion factors between the various units of area per unit volume to $m^2\ m^{-3}$ (SI unit) are given in Table 2.13a.

Table 2.13. Miscellaneous units of area per unit volume (here 1 liter = 1 dm^3)

Unit	$m^2\ m^{-3}$
1 square centimeter per liter ($cm^2\ l^{-1}$)	0.1
1 square decimeter per liter ($dm^2\ l^{-1}$)	10.0
1 square foot per gallon ($ft^2\ gal^{-1}$)	20.435 799
1 square inch per gallon ($in^2\ gal^{-1}$)	0.141 915 3
1 square meter per cubic meter ($m^2\ m^{-3}$)	1.0
1 square meter per liter ($m^2\ l^{-1}$)	1.0×10^3
1 square millimeter per liter ($mm^2\ l^{-1}$)	1.0×10^{-3}
1 square yard per gallon ($yd^2\ gal^{-1}$)	183.9223

2.14 Density (mass per unit volume) (kg m^{-3})

The ratio between the units of mass and units of volume is the density or mass per unit volume.

$$\text{density (kg m}^{-3}\text{)} = \frac{\text{mass (kg)}}{\text{volume (m}^3\text{)}}$$

The term 'specific gravity', which is often used for liquids, is defined as the mass divided by the mass of an equal volume of water at the same temperature. The specific gravity is denoted by Sp. Gr. or *D*: for example, the specific gravity D_4^t means that the liquid substance is weighed at *t* (°C) temperature in relation to the weight of water at 4°C. Thus

$$\text{specific gravity} = \frac{\text{density of a substance}}{\text{density of water at 4°C}}$$

Water at 4°C and normal atmospheric pressure is taken as unity. The exact equality of density and specific gravity is at 4°C only. At any other temperature the density is not equal to the specific gravity.

If water is replaced by another substance, the term relative density is used instead of specific gravity. The specific gravity may be expressed in degree Twaddell or degree Baume. The following simple conversion formulas are used to convert degree Twaddell and degree Baume into specific gravity, and conversely:

$$\text{Sp. Gr.} = 1 + \frac{\text{degree Twaddell}}{200}$$

and

$$\text{Sp. Gr.} = \frac{145}{145 - \text{degree Baume}}$$

or

$$\text{degree Twaddell} = 200\,(\text{Sp. Gr.} - 1)$$

and

$$\text{degree Baume} = 145 - \frac{145}{\text{Sp. Gr.}}$$

Thus the higher the degrees Twaddell or degrees Baume values, the higher the specific gravity of the solution.

For solid materials, the term bulk density is often used. It refers to the total amount of space occupied by a given weight of a dry solid material. It includes the volume of the particles plus the volume of the interparticle voids of the crystals or amorphous solids. In the case of powders one distinguishes between the loose bulk density and the tamped bulk density.

Table 2.14a lists the common units of density found in the technical literature (*see* References) and the conversion factors to kg m^{-3} (SI unit). Interconversion factors for the various units of density are given in Table 2.14b.

The concept of the Amagat unit density is outlined elsewhere (*see* 2.3).

Table 2.14a. Miscellaneous units of density (here 1 liter = 1 dm^3)

Unit	kg m^{-3}
1 dyn per cubic centimeter (dyn cm^{-3})	1.019 716 21
1 grain per cubic foot (gr ft^{-3})	$2.288\,35 \times 10^{-3}$
1 grain per gallon (gr gal^{-1})	
UK	0.014 253 8
US	0.017 118 1
1 grain per milliliter (gr ml^{-1})	64.797 097 6
1 gram per cubic centimeter (g cm^{-3})	1.0×10^3
1 gram per cubic decimeter (g dm^{-3})	1.0
1 gram per cubic meter (g m^{-3})	1.0×10^{-3}
1 gram per liter (g l^{-1})	1.0
1 gram per milliliter (g ml^{-1})	1.0×10^3
1 kilogram per cubic meter (kg m^{-3})	1.0
1 kilogram per liter (kg l^{-1})	1.0×10^3
1 microgram per milliliter (μg ml^{-1})	1.0×10^{-3}
1 milligram per liter (mg l^{-1})	1.0×10^{-3}
1 ounce per gallon (oz gal^{-1})	
UK	6.236 02
US	7.489 15
1 part (weight) per million (volume) (ppm)	1.0×10^{-3}
1 pound per circular mil-foot	$2.936\,929 \times 10^9$
1 pound per cubic foot (lb ft^{-3})	16.0185
1 pound per cubic inch (lb in^{-3})	$2.767\,99 \times 10^4$
1 pound per gallon (lb gal^{-1})	
UK	99.7763
US	119.826
1 poundal per cubic inch (pdl in^{-3})	860.318 66
1 slug per cubic foot	515.38
1 ton (UK) per cubic yard (ton yd^{-3})	$1.328\,94 \times 10^3$

Table 2.14b. Density interconversion factors[a]

from \ to	kg m^{-3}	g cm^{-3}	lb ft^{-3}	lb in^{-3}	lb (UK gal)$^{-1}$	ton yd^{-3}	slug ft^{-3}
1 kilogram per cubic meter (kg m^{-3})	1.0	1.0×10^{-3}	0.062 428	3.6127×10^{-5}	0.010 022	7.5248×10^{-4}	1.9403×10^{-3}
1 gram per cubic centimeter (g cm^{-3})	1.0×10^{3}	1.0	62.428	0.036 127	10.0224	0.752 48	1.9403
1 pound per cubic foot (lb ft^{-3})	16.0185	0.016 018 5	1.0	5.787×10^{-4}	0.160 544	0. 012 053 6	0.031 081
1 pound per cubic inch (lb in^{-3})	$2.767\,99 \times 10^{4}$	27.6799	1.728×10^{3}	1.0	277.419	20.8286	53.707 97
1 pound per gallon (UK) (lb (UK gal)$^{-1}$)	99.7763	0.099 776 3	6.228 84	$3.604\,65 \times 10^{-3}$	1.0	0.075 08	0.1936
1 ton per cubic yard (ton yd^{-3})	$1.328\,94 \times 10^{3}$	1.328 93	82.962	0.048 011	13.318 99	1.0	2.578 571
1 slug per cubic foot (slug ft^{-3})	515.38	0.515 38	32.174	0.018 619 2	5.1654	0.387 811	1.0

a 1 Amagat unit of density = 44.615 77 mol m^{-3} (see page 19)

2.15 Concentration (weight percent)

The concentration may be expressed in various ways: in specific or molar units; in molarity or molality; in mass per volume of solute or solution.

The interconversion factors for concentration are given in Tables 2.15a and 2.15b. The units used to express concentrations are often identical with the units of density (*see* 2.14) and solubility (*see* 2.16).

The common unit of concentration is mole per liter ($mol\ l^{-1}$). The following equalities are useful to remember

$$10^{-3}\ mol\ l^{-1} = 1\ mol\ m^{-3} = 1\ mmol\ l^{-1} = \mu mol\ cm^{-3} = \mu mol\ ml^{-1}$$

Furthermore

$$1\ mol\ l^{-1} = 1\ mol\ dm^{-3}$$

Table 2.15a. Concentration interconversion factors[a]

from \ to	W_2	X_2	m_2	c_2	G_2
weight per cent (W_2)	1.0	$\frac{1000X_2M_2}{X_2M_2+(1-X_2)M_1}$	$\frac{100m_2M_2}{1000+m_2M_2}$	$\frac{c_2M_2}{10d_{12}}$	$\frac{G_2}{10d_{12}}$
mole fraction (X_2)	$\frac{W_2/M_2}{W_2/M_2+(100-W_2)/M_1}$	1.0	$\frac{m_2M_1}{1000+m_2M_1}$	$\frac{c_2M_1}{c_2(M_1-M_2)+1000d_{12}}$	$\frac{G_2M_1}{G_2(M_1-M_2)+1000M_2d_{12}}$
molality (m_2)	$\frac{1000W_2}{M_2(100-W_2)}$	$\frac{1000X_2}{M_1-X_2M_1}$	1.0	$\frac{1000c_2}{1000d_{12}-c_2M_2}$	$\frac{1000G_2}{M_2(1000d_{12}-G_2)}$
molarity (c_2)	$\frac{10d_{12}W_2}{M_2}$	$\frac{1000d_{12}X_2}{X_2M_2+(1-X_2)M_1}$	$\frac{1000d_{12}m_2}{1000+m_2M_2}$	1.0	$\frac{G_2}{M_2}$
grams per liter of solution (G_2)	$10d_{12}W_2$	$\frac{1000d_{12}X_2M_2}{X_2M_2+(1-X_2)M_1}$	$\frac{1000d_{12}m_2M_2}{m_2M_2+1000}$	c_2M_2	1.0

[a] M = molecular weight; d_{12} = density of solution ($g\ cc^{-1}$); subscript 1 = solvent; subscript 2 = solute.

Table 2.15b. Concentration interconversion factor[a]

from \ to	X_2	w_2	θ_2	m_2	c_2
mole fraction (X_2)	1.0	$\frac{w_2 M_1}{w_1 M_2 + w_2 M_1}$	$\frac{\theta_2 V_1^*}{\theta_1 V_2^* + \theta_2 V_1^*}$	$\frac{m_2 M_1}{1000 + m_2 M_1}$	$\frac{c_2 M_1}{c_2(M_1 - M_2) + 1000 d_{12}}$
weight fraction (w_2)	$\frac{X_2 M_2}{X_1 M_1 + X_2 M_2}$	1.0	$\frac{\theta_2 M_1 V_2^*}{M_1 V_2(\theta_2 + \theta_1)}$	$\frac{m_2 M_2}{m_2 M_2 + 1000}$	$\frac{c_2 M_2}{1000 d_{12} - c_2 M_2}$
volume fraction (θ_2)	$\frac{X_2 V_2^*}{X_2 V_2^* + X_1 V_1^*}$	$\frac{w_2 V_2^* M_1}{w_2 V_2^* M_1 + w_1 V_1^* M_2}$	1.0	$\frac{m_2 V_2^* M_1}{m_2 V_2^* M_1 + 1000 V_1^*}$	$\frac{c_2 V_2^* M_1}{c_2 V_2^* M_1 + (1000 d_{12} - c_2 M_2) V_1^*}$
molality (m_2)	$\frac{1000 X_2}{X_1 M_1}$	$\frac{1000 w_2}{w_1 M_2}$	$\frac{1000 \theta_2 V_1^*}{\theta_1 V_2^* M_1}$	1.0	$\frac{1000 c_2}{1000 d_{12} - c_2 M_2}$
molarity (c_2)	$\frac{1000 d_{12} X_2}{X_1 M_1 + X_2 M_2}$	$\frac{1000 d_{12} w_2}{M_2(1 + w_2)}$	$\frac{1000 \theta_2 V_1^* d_{12}}{\theta_1 V_2^* M_1 + \theta_2 V_1^* M_2}$	$\frac{1000 d_{12} m_2}{1000 + m_2 M_2}$	1.0

[a] M = molecular weight; d_{12} = density of the solution (g cc^{-1}); subscript 1 = solvent; subscript 2 = solute.

$$V_2^* = \frac{1}{m_2} \frac{1000 + m_2 M_2}{d_{12}} - \frac{1000}{d_2}$$

2.16 Solubility (mole fraction)

Solubility is a unique quantity which may be expressed by many different units. In addition to the units of solubility, which relate the amount of solute in the solvent, the conditions of the process have to be specified, that is, the temperature and pressure. Furthermore, the pressure given may be partial or total pressure of the system under investigation.

The various definitions and discussions on the units of solubility appear elsewhere (*see* Horvath, 1982). The interconversion factors and formulas between the diverse solubility units are given in Table 2.16.

Table 2.16. Solubility interconversion factors[a]

from \ to	β_2	O_2	T_2	K_2	W_2	X_2
Bunsen coefficient (β_2)	1.0	$\frac{273.15\,O_2}{T}$	$\frac{dT_2}{0.9678}$	dK_2	$\frac{22415zdW_2}{(100-W_2)MP}$	$\frac{22415zdX_2}{(1-X_2)M_L P}$
Ostwald coefficient (O_2)	$\frac{T\beta_2}{273.15}$	1.0	$\frac{dTT_2}{264.35}$	$\frac{dTK_2}{273.15}$	$\frac{22415zdTW_2}{273.15(100-W_2)MP}$	$\frac{22415zdTX_2}{273.15\,(1-X_2)M_L P}$
technical coefficient (T_2)	$\frac{0.9678\beta_2}{d}$	$\frac{264.35\,O_2}{dT}$	1.0	$0.9678K_2$	$\frac{0.9678\;22416zW_2}{(100-W_2)MP}$	$\frac{0.9678\;22415zX_2}{(1-X_2)M_L P}$
Kuenen coefficient (K_2)	$\frac{\beta_2}{d}$	$\frac{273.15\,O_2}{dT}$	$\frac{T_2}{0.9678}$	1.0	$\frac{22415zW_2}{(100-W_2)MP}$	$\frac{0.9678\;22415zX_2}{(1-X_2)M_L P}$
weight percent (W_2)	$\frac{100}{1+(22415zd/MP\beta_2)}$	$\frac{100}{1+(22415zdT/273.15MPO_2)}$	$\frac{100}{1+(22415z\;0.9678/MPT_2)}$	$\frac{100}{1+(22415z/MPK_2)}$	1.0	$\frac{100}{1+[(1-X_2)M_L/MX_2]}$
mole fraction (X_2)	$\frac{1}{1+(22415zd/M_L P\beta_2)}$	$\frac{1}{1+(22415zdT/273.15M_L PO_2)}$	$\frac{1}{1+(22415z\;0.9678/M_L PT_2)}$	$\frac{1}{1+(22415z/M_L PK_2)}$	$\frac{W_2/M}{W_2/M+[(100-W_2)/M_L]}$	1.0

[a] d = density of liquid solvent (g cc^{-1}); z = compressibility factor of gaseous solute; T = absolute temperature (K); P = partial pressure of solute (atm); M = molecular weight of solute; M_L = molecular weight of solvent.

2.17 Henry's law coefficient (H) (N m^{-2} (m.f.)$^{-1}$)

The Henry's law coefficient is the ratio between the partial pressure of the solute gas (P_{part}) and the concentration of the solute in the solvent (usually expressed in mole fraction (m.f.) (X_2) at the specified temperature

$$H = \frac{P_{partial}}{X^2}$$

The following units are commonly used in the technical literature to express Henry's law coefficient:

Unit	N m^{-2} (m.f.)$^{-1}$
1 atmosphere per mole fraction (atm (m.f.)$^{-1}$)	1.013 25 $\times 10^5$
1 bar per mole fraction (bar (m.f.)$^{-1}$)	1.0 $\times 10^5$
1 millimeter mercury per mole fraction (mm Hg (m.f.)$^{-1}$)	133.322
1 newton per square meter mole fraction (Nm^{-2}(m.f.)$^{-1}$)	1.0
1 pascal per mole fraction (Pa (m.f.)$^{-1}$)	1.0

Whereas the interconversion between the various pressure units in the above equation is straightforward, the conversion of the concentration units in the denominator is not direct. The reader is referred to Tables 2.15a and 2.15b for further details.

The Henry's law coefficient (H, mm Hg (m.f.$^{-1}$)) may be calculated from the Bunsen absorption coefficient (β) (*see* Table 2.16) according to the relationship

$$H = \frac{1.70324 \times 10^7 d\ [1 + (MP_{part}\beta / 1.70324 \times 10^7 d)]}{Md}$$

where

d = density of the solvent (g cm^{-3})
M = molecular weight of the solute
P_{part} = partial pressure of the solute over the solution (mm Hg)
β = Bunsen absorption coefficient (N cm^3 (cm^3 - atm)$^{-1}$)

Further relationships between H and other solubility coefficients (e.g., Ostwald, Kuenen, Horiuti, etc.) may be found in Landolt-Börnstein (1976) and Mackay and Shiu (1981).

2.18 Solubility parameter (by Hildebrand) $(J\ m^{-3})^{1/2}$

The solubility parameter or cohesion parameter (cohesive energy density) is expressed as the square root of the ratio between the energy of vaporization and the molar volume at the same temperature

$$\delta = \left(\frac{\Delta E_{vap}}{V_{mol}}\right)^{1/2}$$

where

δ = solubility parameter $((J\ m^{-3})^{1/2})$
ΔE = energy of vaporization $(J\ mol^{-1})$
V_{mol} = molar volume $(m^3\ mol^{-1})$

Comprehensive discussions on the solubility parameter and various cohesion parameters are reported by Hoy (1970) and Barton (1975, 1983).

The interconversion factors for the various units are presented in Table 2.18.

Table 2.18. Solubility parameter interconversion factors

from \ to	$(J\ m^{-3})^{1/2}$	$(J\ cm^{-3})^{1/2}$ or $(MJ\ m^{-3})^{1/2}$ or M pa$^{1/2}$	$(cal\ cm^{-3})^{1/2}$	atm$^{1/2}$
1 $(J\ m^{-3})^{1/2}$	1.0	1.0×10^{-3}	4.8888×10^{-4}	3.1415×10^{-3}
1 { $(J\ cm^{-3})^{1/2}$, $(MJ\ m^{-3})^{1/2}$, M Pa$^{1/2}$ }	1.0×10^{3}	1.0	0.488 88	3.1415
1 $(cal\ cm^{-3})^{1/2}$	2.0455×10^{3}	2.0455	1.0	6.426
1 atm$^{1/2}$	318.316	0.318 316	0.155 62	1.0

2.19 Specific volume $(m^3\ kg^{-1})$

The specific volume is the reciprocal of density (*see* 2.14).

The units used in the technical literature are listed in Table 2.19a. The interconversion factors for the units of specific volume to cubic meter per kilogram $(m^3\ kg^{-1})$ (SI unit) are presented in Table 2.19b.

Table 2.19a. Miscellaneous units of specific volume (here 1 liter = 1 dm^3)

Unit	$m^3\ kg^{-1}$
1 cubic centimeter per gram $(cm^3\ g^{-1})$	1.0×10^{-3}
1 cubic foot per pound $(ft^3\ lb^{-1})$	0.062 428
1 cubic foot per slug $(ft^3\ slug^{-1})$	$1.940\ 32 \times 10^{-3}$
1 cubic foot per ton (UK)	$2.786\ 96 \times 10^{-5}$
1 cubic inch per pound $(in^3\ lb^{-1})$	$3.612\ 73 \times 10^{-5}$
1 cubic meter per kilogram $(m^3\ kg^{-1})$	1.0
1 cubic yard per ton (UK) $(yd^3\ ton^{-1})$	$7.524\ 79 \times 10^{-4}$
1 gallon (UK) per pound (gal (UK) lb^{-1})	0.010 022 4
1 liter per kilogram $(1\ kg^{-1})$	1.0×10^{-3}
1 milliliter per gram $(ml\ g^{-1})$	1.0×10^{-3}

Table 2.19b. Specific volume interconversion factors

from \ to	$m^3\ kg^{-1}$	$ft^3\ lb^{-1}$	gal (UK) lb^{-1}	$ft^3\ slug^{-1}$	$cm^3\ g^{-1}$	yd^3 ton (UK)$^{-1}$	$in^3\ lb^{-1}$
1 cubic meter per kilogram ($m^3\ kg^{-1}$)	1.0	16.0185	99.776	515.38	1.0×10^3	$1.328\ 94 \times 10^3$	2.7679×10^4
1 cubic foot per pound ($ft^3\ lb^{-1}$)	0.062 427 8	1.0	6.228 84	32.174	62.428	82.963	1.728×10^3
1 gallon (UK) per pound (gal (UK) lb^{-1})	0.010 022 4	0.160 544	1.0	5.1654	10.0224	13.3192	227.419
1 cubic foot per slug ($ft^3\ slug^{-1}$)	$1.940\ 32 \times 10^{-3}$	0.031 081	0.1936	1.0	1.9403	2.578 571	53.707 97
1 cubic centimeter per gram ($cm^3\ g^{-1}$)	1.0×10^{-3}	0.016 018 5	0.099 776	0.515 38	1.0	1.328 93	27.6799
1 cubic yard per ton ($yd^3\ ton^{-1}$)	$7.524\ 79 \times 10^{-4}$	0.012 053 6	0.075 08	0.387 811	0.752 48	1.0	20.8286
1 cubic inch per pound ($in^3\ lb^{-1}$)	$3.612\ 73 \times 10^{-5}$	$5.787\ 04 \times 10^{-4}$	$3.604\ 65 \times 10^{-3}$	0.018 619 2	0.036 127	0.048 011	1.0

2.20 Mass rate of flow (kg s^{-1})

The ratio between the units of mass (*see* Table 2.9a) and the units of time (*see* Table 2.5a) is the mass rate of flow.

Some commonly used units are listed in Table 2.20a. The interconversion factors for mass rate of flow are presented in Table 2.20b.

Table 2.20a. Miscellaneous units of mass rate of flow

Unit	kg s^{-1}
1 gram per minute (g min^{-1})	$1.666\,667 \times 10^{-5}$
1 gram per second (g s^{-1})	1.0×10^{-3}
1 kilogram per day (kg d^{-1})	$1.157\,407 \times 10^{-5}$
1 kilogram per hour (kg h^{-1})	$2.777\,778 \times 10^{-4}$
1 kilogram per minute (kg min^{-1})	0.016 666 7
1 kilogram per second (kg s^{-1})	1.0
1 pound per hour (lb h^{-1})	$1.259\,98 \times 10^{-4}$
1 pound per minute (lb min^{-1})	$7.559\,873 \times 10^{-3}$
1 pound per second (lb s^{-1})	0.453 592
1 ton (UK) per hour (ton h^{-1})	0.282 235
1 ton (UK) per minute (ton min^{-1})	16.934 117

Table 2.20b. Mass rate of flow interconversion factors

from \ to	kg s^{-1}	kg h^{-1}	kg min^{-1}	g s^{-1}	lb h^{-1}	lb min^{-1}	lb s^{-1}	ton h^{-1}	ton min^{-1}
1 kilogram per second (kg s^{-1})	1.0	3.6×10^3	60.0	1.0×10^3	$7.936\,643 \times 10^3$	132.2774	2.204 623	3.543 145 2	0.059 052 42
1 kilogram per hour (kg h^{-1})	$2.777\,78 \times 10^{-4}$	1.0	0.016 666 7	0.277 778	2.204 623	0.036 743 72	$6.123\,953 \times 10^{-4}$	$9.842\,07 \times 10^{-4}$	$1.640\,345 \times 10^{-5}$
1 kilogram per minute (kg min^{-1})	0.016 666 7	60.0	1.0	16.666 666 7	132.277 38	2.204 623	0.036 743 716 7	0.059 052 42	$9.842\,07 \times 10^{-4}$
1 gram per second (g s^{-1})	1.0×10^{-3}	3.6	0.06	1.0	7.936 642 8	0.132 277 38	$2.204\,623 \times 10^{-3}$	$3.543\,145 \times 10^{-3}$	$5.905\,242 \times 10^{-5}$
1 pound per hour (lb h^{-1})	$1.259\,979 \times 10^{-4}$	0.453 592 4	$7.559\,873 \times 10^{-3}$	0.125 998	1.0	0.016 666 7	$2.777\,778 \times 10^{-4}$	$4.464\,29 \times 10^{-4}$	$7.440\,483 \times 10^{-6}$
1 pound per minute (lb min^{-1})	$7.559\,873 \times 10^{-3}$	27.215 544	0.453 592 4	7.559 867	60.0	1.0	0.016 666 7	0.026 785 74	$4.464\,29 \times 10^{-4}$
1 pound per second (lb s^{-1})	0.453 592 4	$1.632\,932\,6 \times 10^3$	27.215 544	453.592	3.6×10^3	60.0	1.0	1.607 144 4	0.026 785 74
1 ton (UK) per hour (ton h^{-1})	0.282 235 3	$1.016\,047 \times 10^3$	16.934 117	282.2353	2.24×10^3	37.333 33	0.622 222 22	1.0	0.016 666 667
1 ton (UK) per minute (ton min^{-1})	16.934 117	$6.096\,282 \times 10^4$	$1.016\,047 \times 10^3$	$1.693\,411\,7 \times 10^4$	1.344×10^5	2.240×10^3	37.333 33	60.0	1.0

2.21 Volume rate of flow ($m^3 s^{-1}$)

The ratio between the units of volume given in Table 2.3a and the units of time given in Table 2.5a is the volume rate of flow.

Table 2.21a contains the units which are commonly used in the published literature. The interconversion factors for the units of volume rate of flow are presented in Table 2.21b.

Table 2.21a. Miscellaneous units of volume rate of flow

Unit	$m^3 s^{-1}$
1 acre-foot per day (acre-ft d^{-1})	0.014 276 41
1 acre-foot per hour (acre-ft h^{-1})	0.342 633 8
1 acre-foot per minute (acre-ft min^{-1})	20.558 03
1 acre-foot per second (acre-ft s^{-1})	$1.233\,481\,8 \times 10^3$
1 acre-inch per hour (acre-in h^{-1})	0.028 552 87
1 acre-inch per minute (acre-in min^{-1})	1.713 172 2
1 acre-inch per second (acre-in s^{-1})	102.790 33
1 cubic centimeter per hour ($cm^3 h^{-1}$)	$2.777\,78 \times 10^{-10}$
1 cubic centimeter per minute ($cm^3 min^{-1}$)	$1.666\,67 \times 10^{-8}$
1 cubic centimeter per second ($cm^3 s^{-1}$)	1.0×10^{-6}
1 cubic foot per hour ($ft^3 h^{-1}$)	$7.865\,79 \times 10^{-6}$
1 cubic foot per minute ($ft^3 min^{-1}$)	$4.719\,474 \times 10^{-4}$
1 cubic foot per second (cusec) ($ft^3 s^{-1}$)	0.028 316 8
1 cubic inch per hour ($in^3 h^{-1}$)	$4.551\,962\,2 \times 10^{-9}$
1 cubic inch per minute ($in^3 min^{-1}$)	$2.731\,177\,3 \times 10^{-7}$
1 cubic inch per second ($in^3 s^{-1}$)	$1.638\,706\,4\ 10^{-5}$
1 cubic meter per hour ($m^3 h^{-1}$)	$2.777\,78 \times 10^{-4}$
1 cubic meter per minute ($m^3 min^{-1}$)	0.016 666 7
1 cubic meter per second (cumec) ($m^3 s^{-1}$)	1.0
1 cubic yard per minute ($yd^3 min^{-1}$)	0.012 742 5
1 cumec (cubic meter per second) ($m^3 s^{-1}$)	1.0
1 cusec (cubic foot per second) ($ft^3 s^{-1}$)	0.028 316 8
1 gallon per day (gal day^{-1})	
UK	$5.261\,678 \times 10^{-8}$
US	$4.381\,264 \times 10^{-8}$
1 gallon per hour (gal h^{-1})	
UK	$1.262\,80 \times 10^{-6}$
US	$1.051\,503 \times 10^{-6}$
1 gallon per minute (gal min^{-1})	
UK	$7.576\,82 \times 10^{-5}$
US	$6.309\,020 \times 10^{-5}$
1 gallon per second (gal s^{-1})	
UK	$4.546\,09 \times 10^{-3}$
US	$3.785\,412 \times 10^{-3}$
1 liter per hour ($1\ h^{-1}$)	$2.777\,78 \times 10^{-7}$
1 liter per minute ($1\ min^{-1}$)	$1.666\,67 \times 10^{-5}$
1 liter per second ($1\ s^{-1}$)	1.0×10^{-3}

Table 2.21b. Volume rate of flow interconversion factors (here 1 liter (1901) = 1.000 023 dm^3)

from \ to	$cm^3\ s^{-3}$	$l\ min^{-1}$	$m^3\ s^{-1}$	$gal\ min^{-1}$	$ft^3\ min^{-1}$	$l\ s^{-1}$	$gal\ s^{-1}$	$yd^3\ min^{-1}$	$ft^3\ s^{-1}$
1 cubic centimeter per second ($cm^3\ s^{-1}$)	1.0	0.059 998 3	1.0×10^{-6}	0.015 850 3	$2.118\ 88 \times 10^{-3}$	$9.999\ 72 \times 10^{-4}$	$2.641\ 72 \times 10^{-4}$	$7.847\ 70 \times 10^{-5}$	$3.531\ 47 \times 10^{-5}$
1 liter per minute ($l\ min^{-1}$)	16.667 13	1.0	$1.666\ 714 \times 10^{-5}$	0.264 179 4	0.035 315 7	0.016 666 7	$4.402\ 99 \times 10^{-3}$	$1.307\ 99 \times 10^{-3}$	$5.885\ 94 \times 10^{-4}$
1 cubic meter per second ($m^3\ s^{-1}$)	1.0×10^{-6}	$5.999\ 83 \times 10^{4}$	1.0	$1.585\ 03 \times 10^{4}$	$2.118\ 88 \times 10^{3}$	999.972	264.172	78.477 02	35.314 68
1 gallon (US) per minute ($gal\ min^{-1}$)	63.0902	3.785 306	$6.309\ 02 \times 10^{-5}$	1.0	0.133 680 6	0.063 088 4	0.016 666 7	$4.951\ 13 \times 10^{-3}$	$2.228\ 01 \times 10^{-3}$
1 cubic foot per minute ($ft^3\ min^{-1}$)	471.947	28.316 05	$4.719\ 48 \times 10^{-4}$	7.480 519	1.0	0.471 934 2	0.124 675 3	0.037 037	0.016 666 7
1 liter per second ($l\ s^{-1}$)	$1.000\ 028 \times 10^{3}$	60.0	$1.000\ 028 \times 10^{-3}$	15.850 77	2.118 939	1.0	0.264 179 4	0.078 479 2	0.035 315 7
1 gallon (US) per second ($gal\ s^{-1}$)	$3.785\ 412 \times 10^{3}$	227.1183	$3.785\ 412 \times 10^{-3}$	60.0	8.020 833	3.785 306	1.0	0.297 067 9	0.133 680 6
1 cubic yard per minute ($yd^3\ min^{-1}$)	$1.274\ 258 \times 10^{4}$	764.534	0.012 742 58	201.974	27.0	12.742 22	3.366 234	1.0	0.45
1 cubic foot per second ($ft^3\ s^{-1}$)	$2.831\ 685 \times 10^{4}$	$1.698\ 96 \times 10^{3}$	0.028 316 8	448.831	60.0	28.316 05	7.480 519	2.222 222	1.0

2.22 Fuel consumption ($m^3\ m^{-1}$)

The fuel consumption may be expressed as volume per distance (European traffic) or distance per volume (UK and US traffic).

The various interconversion factors for fuel consumption (European traffic) are presented in Table 2.22. To calculate the distance per volume factors (UK and US traffic) from Table 2.22 take the reciprocal of the corresponding units.

Table 2.22. Fuel consumption interconversion factors (1 liter (1901) = 1.000 028 liter)

from \ to	gal (US) $mile^{-1}$	pt $mile^{-1}$	$ft^3\ mile^{-1}$	gal (US) yd^{-1}	l m^{-1}	l km^{-1}	$m^3\ m^{-1}$	$m^3\ km^{-1}$	gal (UK) $mile^{-1}$
1 gallon (US) per mile (gal (US) $mile^{-1}$)	1.0	8.0	0.133 681	$5.681\ 818 \times 10^{-4}$	$2.352\ 086 \times 10^{-3}$	2.352 086	$2.352\ 15 \times 10^{-6}$	$2.352\ 151 \times 10^{-3}$	0.832 674
1 pint per mile (pt $mile^{-1}$)	0.125	1.0	0.016 71	$7.102\ 273 \times 10^{-5}$	$2.940\ 107 \times 10^{-4}$	0.294 010 7	$2.940\ 187 \times 10^{-7}$	$2.940\ 187 \times 10^{-4}$	0.104 084 3
1 cubic foot per mile ($ft^3\ mile^{-1}$)	7.480 519	59.844 16	1.0	$4.250\ 295 \times 10^{-3}$	0.017 594 82	17.594 82	$1.759\ 535 \times 10^{-5}$	0.017 595 35	6.228 848
1 gallon (US) per yard (gal (US) yd^{-1})	1.76×10^3	$1.408\ 004 \times 10^4$	235.2793	1.0	4.139 661	$4.139\ 661 \times 10^3$	$4.139\ 775 \times 10^{-3}$	4.139 775	$1.465\ 506\ 5 \times 10^3$
1 liter* per meter (l m^{-1})	425.1557	$3.401\ 258\ 5 \times 10^3$	56.835 127	0.241 565 34	1.0	1.0×10^3	$1.000\ 028 \times 10^{-3}$	1.000 028	354.006 11
1 liter* per kilometer (l km^{-1})	0.425 155 7	3.401 258 5	0.056 835 122	$2.415\ 653\ 4 \times 10^{-4}$	1.0×10^{-3}	1.0	$1.000\ 028 \times 10^{-6}$	$1.000\ 028 \times 10^{-3}$	0.354 006
1 cubic meter per meter ($m^3\ m^{-1}$)	$4.251\ 444\ 4 \times 10^5$	$3.401\ 258\ 5 \times 10^6$	$5.683\ 356 \times 10^4$	241.565 34	999.972	$9.999\ 72 \times 10^5$	1.0	1.0×10^3	$3.540\ 06 \times 10^5$
1 cubic meter per kilometer ($m^3\ km^{-1}$)	425.144 44	$3.401\ 258\ 5 \times 10^3$	56.833 56	0.241 565 34	0.999 972	999.972	1.0×10^{-3}	1.0	354.006
1 gallon (UK) per mile (gal (UK) $mile^{-1}$)	1.200 95	9.6076	0.160 543 3	$6.823\ 579 \times 10^{-4}$	$2.824\ 81 \times 10^{-3}$	2.824 81	$2.824\ 81 \times 10^{-6}$	$2.824\ 81 \times 10^{-3}$	1.0

2.23 Moment of inertia (kg m^2)

Moment of inertia is the product of mass (*see* Table 2.9a) and length (*see* Table 2.1a) squared.

The moment of inertia may be expressed in several units (*see* Table 2.23a). The interconversion factors for units of moment of inertia are given in Table 2.23b.

Table 2.23a. Miscellaneous units of moment of inertia

Unit	kg m^2
1 gram centimeter squared (g cm^2)	1.0×10^{-7}
1 gram decimeter squared (g dm^2)	1.0×10^{-5}
1 gram meter squared (g m^2)	1.0×10^{-3}
1 gram millimeter squared (g mm^2)	1.0×10^{-9}
1 kilogram centimeter squared (kg cm^2)	1.0×10^{-4}
1 kilogram decimeter squared (kg dm^2)	1.0×10^{-2}
1 kilogram meter squared (kg m^2)	1.0
1 kilogram millimeter squared (kg mm^2)	1.0×10^{-6}
1 ounce foot squared (oz ft^2)	$2.633\,76 \times 10^{-3}$
1 ounce inch squared (oz in^2)	$1.829\,00 \times 10^{-5}$
1 pound foot squared (lb ft^2)	0.042 140 1
1 pound inch squared (lb in^2)	$2.926\,40 \times 10^{-4}$
1 pound yard squared (lb yd^2)	0.379 260 85
1 ton (UK) foot squared (ton ft^2)	94.393 805
1 tonne meter squared (t m^2)	1.0×10^{3}

Table 2.23b. Moments of inertia interconversion factors

from \ to	lb ft^2	oz in^2	lb in^2	lb yd^2	kg cm^2	kg m^2	kg mm^2	t m^2	ton ft^2
1 pound foot squared (lb ft^2)	1.0	$2.304\,00 \times 10^3$	144.0	0.111 111 11	421.400 95	0.042 140 095	$4.214\,009\,5 \times 10^4$	$4.214\,009\,5 \times 10^{-5}$	$4.464\,29 \times 10^{-4}$
1 ounce inch squared (oz in^2)	$4.340\,277\,8 \times 10^{-4}$	1.0	0.0625	$4.822\,531\,3 \times 10^{-5}$	0.182 899 76	$1.828\,997\,6 \times 10^{-5}$	18.289 976 32	$1.828\,997\,6 \times 10^{-8}$	$1.937\,625 \times 10^{-7}$
1 pound inch squared (lb in^2)	$6.944\,444\,4 \times 10^{-3}$	16.0	1.0	$7.716\,05 \times 10^{-4}$	2.926 396 7	$2.926\,396\,7 \times 10^{-4}$	292.639 67	$2.926\,396\,7 \times 10^{-7}$	$3.100\,201\,2 \times 10^{-6}$
1 pound yard squared (lb yd^2)	9.0	$2.073\,599\,8 \times 10^4$	1.296×10^3	1.0	$3.792\,608\,5 \times 10^3$	0.379 260 85	$3.792\,608\,5 \times 10^5$	$3.792\,608\,5 \times 10^{-4}$	$4.017\,861 \times 10^{-3}$
1 kilogram centimeter squared (kg cm^2)	$2.373\,036\,91 \times 10^{-3}$	5.467 475 64	0.341 717 167	$2.636\,707\,7 \times 10^{-4}$	1.0	1.0×10^{-4}	100.0	1.0×10^{-7}	$1.059\,390\,57 \times 10^{-6}$
1 kilogram meter squared (kg m^2)	23.730 369	$5.467\,475\,64 \times 10^4$	$3.417\,171\,67 \times 10^3$	2.636 707 7	1.0×10^4	1.0	1.0×10^6	1.0×10^{-3}	0.010 593 905 7
1 kilogram millimeter squared (kg mm^2)	$2.373\,036\,9 \times 10^{-5}$	0.054 674 756	$3.417\,171\,67 \times 10^{-3}$	$2.636\,707\,7 \times 10^{-6}$	0.0100	1.0×10^{-6}	1.0	1.0×10^{-9}	$1.059\,390\,57 \times 10^{-8}$
1 tonne meter squared **metric (t m^2)**	$2.373\,036\,9 \times 10^4$	$5.467\,475\,6 \times 10^7$	$3.417\,171\,67 \times 10^6$	$2.636\,707\,7 \times 10^3$	1.0×10^7	1.0×10^3	1.0×10^9	1.0	10.593 905 7
1 ton (UK) foot squared (t m^2)	$2.239\,997\,9 \times 10^3$	$5.160\,957\,39 \times 10^6$	$3.225\,597\,1 \times 10^5$	248.888 65	$9.439\,389\,3 \times 10^5$	94.393 893	$9.439\,389\,3 \times 10^7$	0.094 393 893	1.0

2.24 Moment of force (torque) (N m)

The product of force and length is the moment of force. The direction of the force and length components is perpendicular to each other (compare with energy).

The various units of the moment of force are outlined in Table 2.24a. The interconversion factors between the different units are given in Table 2.24b.

Table 2.24a. Miscellaneous units of moment of force

Unit	N m
1 dyne-centimeter (or erg) (dyn-cm)	1.0×10^{-7}
1 erg (or dyne-centimeter)	1.0×10^{-7}
1 gram-force centimeter (gf cm)	$9.806\ 65 \times 10^{-5}$
1 kilogram-force centimeter (kgf cm)	0.098 066 5
1 kilogram-force meter (kgf m or kp m)	9.806 65
1 newton centimeter (N cm)	0.01
1 newton meter (N m)	1.0
1 ounce-force inch (ozf in)	$7.061\ 55 \times 10^{-3}$
1 pound-force foot (lbf ft)	1.335 82
1 pound-force inch (or inch pound) (lbf in)	0.112 985
1 pound-force yard (lbf yd)	4.067 452 3
1 poundal foot (or foot-poundal) (pdl ft)	0.042 140
1 ton (short)-force foot (short tonf ft)	$2.711\ 634\ 9 \times 10^{3}$
1 ton (UK)-force foot (tonf ft)	$3.037\ 033 \times 10^{3}$
1 tonne-force meter (tf m)	$9.806\ 65 \times 10^{3}$

Table 2.24b. Moment of force (torque) interconversion factors

from \ to	N m	kgf m	kgf cm	lbf yd	lbf ft	lbf in	N cm	tonf ft	short tonf ft	tonnef m
1 newton meter (N m)	1.0	0.101 971 6	10.197 16	0.245 854	0.737 562 4	8.850 748 3	100.0	$3.292\,687 \times 10^{-4}$	$3.687\,795 \times 10^{-4}$	$1.019\,716 \times 10^{-4}$
1 kilogram-force meter (kgf m)	9.806 65	1.0	100.0	2.411 003 9	7.233 014	86.796 168 1	980.665	$3.229\,025\,7 \times 10^{-3}$	$3.616\,506 \times 10^{-3}$	1.0×10^{-3}
1 kilogram-force centimeter (kgf cm)	0.098 066 5	0.01	1.0	0.024 110 039	0.072 330 14	0.867 961 681	9.806 65	$3.229\,025\,7 \times 10^{-5}$	$3.616\,506 \times 10^{-5}$	1.0×10^{-5}
1 pound-force yard (lbf yd)	4.067 452 3	0.414 764 86	41.476 486	1.0	3.0	36.0	406.7452	$1.339\,285\,8 \times 10^{-3}$	1.5×10^{-3}	$4.147\,648\,6 \times 10^{-4}$
1 pound-force foot (lbf ft)	1.355 82	0.138 254 95	13.825 495	0.333 333 333	1.0	12.0	135.581 746	$4.464\,286 \times 10^{-4}$	5.0×10^{-4}	$1.382\,549\,5 \times 10^{-4}$
1 pound-force inch (lbf in)	0.112 985	0.011 521 246	1.152 124 6	0.027 777 777 8	0.083 333	1.0	11.298 478 8	$3.720\,238\,19 \times 10^{-5}$	$4.166\,667 \times 10^{-5}$	$1.152\,125 \times 10^{-5}$
1 newton centimeter (N cm)	0.01	$1.019\,716 \times 10^{-3}$	0.101 971 6	$2.458\,540\,4 \times 10^{-3}$	$7.375\,623\,6 \times 10^{-3}$	0.088 507 483	1.0	$3.292\,687 \times 10^{-6}$	$3.687\,795\,4 \times 10^{-6}$	$1.019\,716 \times 10^{-6}$
1 ton (UK)-force foot (tonf ft)	$3.037\,033 \times 10^{3}$	309.691	$3.096\,91 \times 10^{4}$	746.667	2.24×10^{3}	2.688×10^{4}	$3.037\,033 \times 10^{5}$	1.0	1.12	0.309 691 1
1 ton (US short)-force foot (short tonf ft)	$2.711\,634\,9 \times 10^{3}$	276.5099	$2.765\,099 \times 10^{4}$	666.667	2.0×10^{3}	2.4×10^{4}	$2.711\,634\,9 \times 10^{5}$	0.892 857 1	1.0	0.276 509 91
1 tonne-force meter (tonnef m)	$9.806\,65 \times 10^{3}$	1.0×10^{3}	1.0×10^{5}	$2.411\,003\,9 \times 10^{3}$	$7.233\,014 \times 10^{3}$	$8.679\,616\,8 \times 10^{4}$	$9.806\,65 \times 10^{5}$	3.229 024 15	3.616 506	1.0

2.25 Momentum (linear and angular) ($kg\ m\ s^{-1}$ and $kg\ m^2\ s^{-1}$)

The linear or translational momentum of a particle is defined as the product of the mass and velocity. The following common units are in use:

Unit	$kg\ m\ s^{-1}$
1 gram centimeter per second ($g\ cm\ s^{-1}$)	1.0×10^{-5}
1 kilogram meter per second ($kg\ m\ s^{-1}$)	1.0
1 pound foot per second ($lb\ ft\ s^{-1}$)	0.138 255

The angular momentum of a particle about a point is the vector product of the radius vector from the point to the particle and the momentum of the particle. The angular momentum may be expressed in $kg\ m^2\ s^{-1}$ or $lb\ ft^2\ s^{-1}$. The conversion factor is

$$1\ lb\ ft^2\ s^{-1} = 0.042\ 140\ 1\ kg\ m^2\ s^{-1}$$

2.26 Force (N)

The force is defined as the product of the mass and acceleration.

The various units for force reported in the technical literature are summarized in Table 2.26a. The interconversion factors between various units are given in Table 2.26b.

Table 2.26a. Miscellaneous units of force

Unit	N
1 dyne (or dyn) ($g\ cm\ s^{-2}$)	1.0×10^{-5}
1 grain-force	$6.354\ 601 \times 10^{-4}$
1 gram-force (gf)	$9.806\ 65 \times 10^{-3}$
1 kilogram-force (or kilopond) (kgf or kp)	9.806 65
1 kip (US)	$4.448\ 22 \times 10^{3}$
1 newton (N) ($kg\ m\ s^{-2}$)	1.0
1 ounce-force (ozf)	0.278 014
1 pound-force (lbf)	4.448 22
1 poundal (pdl)	0.138 255
1 sthéne ($t\ m\ s^{-2}$)	1.0×10^{3}
1 ton (metric)-force	$9.806\ 65 \times 10^{3}$
1 ton (UK)-force	$9.964\ 02 \times 10^{3}$
1 ton (US)-force	$8.896\ 44 \times 10^{3}$

Table 2.26b. Force interconversion factors

from \ to	N (kg m s^{-2})	kgf (kp)	lbf	dyn (g cm s^{-2})	tonf (UK)	tonf (US)	tonnef
1 newton (N) (kg m s^{-2})	1.0	0.101 971 6	0.224 809	1.0×10^{5}	$1.003\ 611 \times 10^{-4}$	$1.124\ 04 \times 10^{-4}$	$1.019\ 716 \times 10^{-4}$
1 kilogram-force (or kilopond) (kgf or kp)	9.806 65	1.0	2.204 622 6	$9.806\ 65 \times 10^{5}$	$9.842\ 07 \times 10^{-4}$	$1.102\ 311 \times 10^{-3}$	1.0×10^{-3}
1 pound-force (lbf)	4.448 22	0.453 592 37	1.0	$4.448\ 22 \times 10^{5}$	$4.464\ 286 \times 10^{-4}$	5.0×10^{-4}	$4.535\ 923\ 7 \times 10^{-4}$
1 dyne (or dyn) (g cm s^{-2})	1.0×10^{-5}	$1.019\ 716 \times 10^{-6}$	$2.248\ 09 \times 10^{-6}$	1.0	$1.003\ 610\ 9 \times 10^{-9}$	$1.124\ 04 \times 10^{-9}$	$1.019\ 716 \times 10^{-9}$
1 ton (UK)-force (tonf (UK, long))	$9.964\ 02 \times 10^{3}$	$1.016\ 047 \times 10^{3}$	2.24×10^{3}	$9.964\ 02 \times 10^{8}$	1.0	1.12	1.016 046 9
1 ton (US)-force (tonf (USA, short))	$8.896\ 44 \times 10^{3}$	907.184 74	2.0×10^{3}	$8.896\ 44 \times 10^{8}$	0.892 857 1	1.0	0.907 184 74
1 tonne-force (tonnef)	$9.806\ 65 \times 10^{3}$	1.0×10^{3}	$2.204\ 622\ 6 \times 10^{3}$	$9.806\ 65 \times 10^{8}$	0.984 206 53	1.102 311	1.0

2.27 Pressure (stress) (N m^{-2})

Pressure or stress is the ratio between force and area.

The various units of pressure compiled from the technical literature are summarized in Table 2.27a. The interconversion factors between the units are given in Table 2.27b.

The absolute and gauge pressures are denoted by the extra 'a' and 'g' letters, respectively (e.g., psia (pound per square inch absolute) or psig (pound per square inch gauge)). The conversion between the absolute and gauge pressures is as follows:

$$1 \text{ psig} = 1 \text{ psia} + 14.6959$$

$$1 \text{ atm gauge} = 1 \text{ atm absolute} + 1$$

1 atmosphere means that the atmospheric pressure is the datum.

In German, the symbol for technical atmosphere is 'at' and 'atü' or 'ata' stands for gauge.

Table 2.27a. Miscellaneous units of pressure

Unit	N m^{-2}
1 atmosphere (absolute) (atm)	$1.013\,25 \times 10^5$
1 bar	1.0×10^5
1 barye (or dyne per square centimeter)	0.1
1 centimeter of mercury at 0°C (cm Hg)	$1.333\,22 \times 10^3$
1 centimeter of water at 4°C (cm H_2O)	98.0638
1 dyne per square centimeter (or barye) (dyn cm^{-2})	0.1
1 foot of air at 1 atm and 60°F	3.654 223
1 foot of water at 39.2°F	$2.989\,07 \times 10^3$
1 gram-force per square centimeter (gf cm^{-2})	98.0665
1 hectobar (hbar)	1.0×10^{-7}
1 inch of water at 4°C (in H_2O)	249.089
1 inch of mercury at 32°F (in Hg)	$3.386\,39 \times 10^3$
1 kilogram-force (or kilopond) per centimeter squared (kgf cm^{-2})	$9.806\,65 \times 10^4$
1 kilogram-force (or kilopond) per meter squared (kgf m^{-2})	9.806 65
1 kilogram-force (or kilopond) per millimeter squared (kgf mm^{-2})	$9.806\,65 \times 10^6$
1 kilonewton per square meter (kN m^{-2})	1.0×10^3
1 kips per square inch (ksi)	$6.894\,76 \times 10^6$
1 meganewton per square meter (MN m^{-2})	1.0×10^6
1 meter of water at 4°C (m H_2O)	$9.806\,65 \times 10^3$
1 millibar (mbar)	100.0
1 millimeter of mercury at 0°C (mm Hg)	133.322
1 millimeter of water at 4°C (mm H_2O)	9.806 65
1 newton per square meter (or pascal) (N m^{-2} or Pa)	1.0
1 newton per square millimeter (N mm^{-2})	1.0×10^6
1 ounce per square foot (oz ft^{-2})	2.992 599 27
1 ounce per square inch (oz in^{-2})	430.934 916
1 pascal (Pa)	1.0
1 piéze (pz)	1.0×10^3
1 pound-force per square foot (lbf ft^{-2})	47.8803
1 pound-force per square inch (psi) (lbf in^{-2})	$6.894\,76 \times 10^3$
1 poundal per square foot (pdl ft^{-2})	1.448 16
1 sthéne per square meter (sn m^{-2})	1.0×10^3
1 technical atmosphere (absolute) (at)	$9.806\,65 \times 10^4$
1 ton (US)-force per square foot	$9.576\,05 \times 10^4$
1 ton (US)-force per square inch	$1.378\,95 \times 10^7$
1 ton (UK)-force per square foot	$1.072\,52 \times 10^5$
1 ton (UK)-force per square inch	$1.544\,43 \times 10^7$
1 torr (or tor)	133.322

Table 2.27b. Pressure (stress) interconversion factors

from \ to	N m^{-2} (Pa)	bar	atm	mm Hg	in H_2O	in Hg	lbf in^{-2}	lbf ft^{-2}	dyn cm^{-2}	kgf cm^{-2}
1 newton per square meter (Nm^{-1}) (or pascal, Pa)	1.0	1.0×10^{-5}	9.86923×10^{-6}	$7.500\,62 \times 10^{-3}$	$4.014\,63 \times 10^{-3}$	2.953×10^{-4}	1.45038×10^{-4}	2.208854×10^{-2}	10.0	1.01972×10^{-5}
1 bar (bar)	1.0×10^{5}	1.0	0.986 923	750.062	401.463	29.53	14.5038	2.08854×10^{3}	1.0×10^{6}	1.01972
1 atmosphere (atm)	$1.013\,25 \times 10^{5}$	1.013 25	1.0	760.0	406.8	29.9213	14.6959	$2.116\,22 \times 10^{3}$	$1.013\,25 \times 10^{6}$	1.033 23
1 millimeter of mercury at 0°C (mm Hg)	133.322	$1.333\,22 \times 10^{-3}$	$1.315\,79 \times 10^{-3}$	1.0	0.535 24	0.039 3701	0.019 336 8	2.78450	$1.333\,22 \times 10^{3}$	$1.359\,51 \times 10^{-3}$
1 inch of water at 4°C (in H_2O)	249.089	2.49089×10^{-3}	2.458×10^{-3}	1.86832	1.0	0.073 556	0.036 127	5.20233	2.49089×10^{3}	2.54×10^{-3}
1 inch of mercury at 32°F (in Hg)	3.3864×10^{3}	0.033 864	0.033 421	25.40	13.5951	1.0	0.491 16	70.7263	3.3864×10^{4}	0.034 532
1 pound-force per square inch (psi) (lbf in^{-2})	6.89476×10^{3}	0.068 9476	0.068 046	51.7149	27.68	2.036	1.0	144.0	$6.894\,76 \times 10^{4}$	0.070 307
1 pound-force per square foot (lbf ft^{-2})	47.8803	$4.788\,03 \times 10^{-4}$	$4.725\,41 \times 10^{-4}$	0.359 131	0.192 222	0.014 139	6.9444×10^{-3}	1.0	478.003	$4.882\,43 \times 10^{-4}$
1 dyne per square centimeter (dyn cm^{-2})	0.1	1.0×10^{-6}	$9.869\,23 \times 10^{-7}$	$7.500\,62 \times 10^{-4}$	4.015×10^{-4}	2.953×10^{-5}	1.45038×10^{-5}	$2.088\,54 \times 10^{-3}$	1.0	$1.019\,72 \times 10^{-6}$
1 kilogram-force per square centimeter (kgf cm^{-2})	$9.806\,65 \times 10^{4}$	0.980 665	0.967 841	735.559	393.7	28.959	14.2233	$2.048\,16 \times 10^{3}$	$9.806\,65 \times 10^{5}$	1.0

2.28 Viscosity (dynamic) or absolute viscosity ($N\ s\ m^{-2}$)

The dynamic viscosity is the ratio between the stress and velocity gradient.

The units commonly used in the technical literature are listed in Table 2.28a. The interconversion factors for dynamic viscosity are given in Table 2.28b.

Table 2.28a. Miscellaneous units of dynamic viscosity

Unit	$N\ s\ m^{-2}$
1 centipoise (cP)	1.0×10^{-3}
1 cgs unit of absolute viscosity (or poise)	0.1
1 dyne second per meter square (dyn s m^{-2})	0.1
1 gram per centimeter second (or poise) (g cm^{-1} s^{-1})	0.1
1 gram-second per square centimeter	98.0665
1 kilogram per meter hour (kg m^{-1} h^{-1})	$2.777\ 778 \times 10^{-4}$
1 kilogram per meter second (kg m^{-1} s^{-1})	1.0
1 kilogram-force second per square meter (kgf s m^{-2})	9.806 65
1 newton second per square meter (N s m^{-2})	1.0
1 pascal second (Pa s)	1.0
1 poise (or gram per centimeter second) (P)	0.1
1 poiseuille (in France) (Pl)	1.0
1 pound per foot hour (lb ft^{-1} h^{-1})	$4.133\ 79 \times 10^{-4}$
1 pound per foot second (lb ft^{-1} s^{-1})	1.488 16
1 pound-force hour per square foot (lbf h ft^{-2})	$1.723\ 69 \times 10^{5}$
1 pound-force second per square foot (lbf s ft^{-2})	47.8803
1 pound-force second per square inch (reyn)	$6.894\ 76 \times 10^{3}$
1 pound-force second per square inch (lbf s in^{-2})	$6.894\ 76 \times 10^{3}$
1 poundal second per square foot (pdl s ft^{-2})	1.488 16
1 reyn (or pound-force second per square inch)	$6.894\ 76 \times 10^{3}$
1 slug hour per foot second squared	$1.723\ 69 \times 10^{5}$
1 slug per foot second	47.8803
1 stoke per density in gram per milliliter	0.1

Table 2.28b. Viscosity (absolute or dynamic) interconversion factors

from \ to	$N\ s\ m^{-2}$	P	cP	$kg\ m^{-1}\ h^{-1}$	$lb\ ft^{-1}\ s^{-1}$	$kgf\ s\ m^{-2}$	$lbf\ s\ ft^{-2}$	$lb\ ft^{-1}\ h^{-1}$	$lbf\ h\ ft^{-2}$
1 newton second per square meter ($N\ s\ m^{-2}$)	1.0	10.0	1.0×10^{3}	3.6×10^{3}	0.671 97	0.101 972	0.020 885 4	$2.419\ 09 \times 10^{3}$	$5.801\ 38 \times 10^{-6}$
1 poise (P)	0.1	1.0	100.0	360.0	0.067 197	0.010 197 2	$2.088\ 54 \times 10^{-3}$	241.909	$5.801\ 38 \times 10^{-7}$
1 centipoise (cP)	1.0×10^{-3}	0.01	1.0	3.6	6.7197×10^{-4}	$1.019\ 72 \times 10^{-4}$	$2.088\ 54 \times 10^{-5}$	2.419 09	$5.801\ 38 \times 10^{-9}$
1 kilogram per meter hour ($kg\ m^{-1}\ h^{-1}$)	$2.777\ 778 \times 10^{-4}$	$2.777\ 778 \times 10^{-3}$	0.277 777 8	1.0	$1.866\ 58 \times 10^{-4}$	$2.832\ 55 \times 10^{-5}$	$5.801\ 51 \times 10^{-6}$	0.671 969	$1.611\ 528 \times 10^{-9}$
1 pound per foot second ($lb\ ft^{-1}\ s^{-1}$)	1.488 16	14.8816	$1.488\ 16 \times 10^{3}$	$5.357\ 39 \times 10^{3}$	1.0	0.151 75	0.031 081	3.6×10^{3}	$8.633\ 611 \times 10^{-6}$
1 kilogram-force second per square meter ($kgf\ s\ m^{-2}$)	9.806 65	98.0665	$9.806\ 65 \times 10^{3}$	$3.530\ 39 \times 10^{4}$	6.589 76	1.0	0.204 816	$2.372\ 31 \times 10^{4}$	$5.689\ 333 \times 10^{-5}$
1 pound-force second per square foot ($lbf\ s\ ft^{-2}$)	47.8803	478.803	$4.788\ 03 \times 10^{4}$	$1.723\ 69 \times 10^{5}$	32.174	4.882 43	1.0	$1.158\ 27 \times 10^{5}$	$2.777\ 778 \times 10^{-4}$
1 pound per foot hour ($lb\ ft^{-1}\ h^{-1}$)	$4.133\ 79 \times 10^{-4}$	$4.133\ 79 \times 10^{-3}$	0.413 379	1.488 16	$2.777\ 778 \times 10^{-4}$	$4.215\ 29 \times 10^{-5}$	8.6336×10^{-6}	1.0	$2.398\ 222 \times 10^{-9}$
1 pound-force hour per square foot ($lbf\ h\ ft^{-2}$)	$1.723\ 69 \times 10^{5}$	$1.723\ 69 \times 10^{6}$	$1.723\ 69 \times 10^{8}$	6.205×10^{8}	$1.158\ 27 \times 10^{5}$	1.758×10^{4}	3.6×10^{3}	4.17×10^{8}	1.0

2.29 Viscosity (kinematic) or thermal diffusivity ($m^2\ s^{-1}$)

The kinematic viscosity is the ratio between the length squared and time. The same units may be used to express the thermal diffusivity.

The common units used to express the kinematic viscosity are listed in Table 2.29a. The interconversion factors for the units of kinematic viscosity are presented in Table 2.29b.

Table 2.29a. Miscellaneous units of kinematic viscosity

Unit	$m^2\ s^{-1}$
1 centimeter squared per hour ($cm^2\ h^{-1}$)	$2.777\,778 \times 10^{-8}$
1 centimeter squared per minute ($cm^2\ min^{-1}$)	$1.666\,667 \times 10^{-6}$
1 centimeter squared per second ($cm^2\ s^{-1}$)	1.0×10^{-4}
1 centistokes (cSt)	1.0×10^{-6}
1 cgs unit of kinematic viscosity (stokes)	1.0×10^{-4}
1 foot squared per hour ($ft^2\ h^{-1}$)	$2.580\,64 \times 10^{-5}$
1 foot squared per minute ($ft^2\ min^{-1}$)	$1.548\,383\,3 \times 10^{-3}$
1 foot squared per second ($ft^2\ s^{-1}$)	0.092 903
1 inch squared per hour ($in^2\ h^{-1}$)	$1.792\,11 \times 10^{-7}$
1 inch squared per second ($in^2\ s^{-1}$)	6.4516×10^{-4}
1 meter squared per hour ($m^2\ h^{-1}$)	$2.777\,778 \times 10^{-4}$
1 meter squared per minute ($m^2\ min^{-1}$)	0.016 666 67
1 meter squared per second ($m^2\ s^{-1}$)	1.0
1 millimeter squared per second ($mm^2\ s^{-1}$)	1.0×10^{-6}
1 poise-cubic centimeter per gram ($Pcm^3\ g^{-1}$)	1.0×10^{-4}
1 poise-cubic foot per pound ($Pft^3\ lb^{-1}$)	$6.242\,796 \times 10^{-3}$
1 poise-cubic inch per gram ($Pin^3\ g^{-1}$)	$1.638\,706\,4 \times 10^{-3}$
1 stokes (cgs unit of kinematic viscosity) (St)	1.0×10^{-4}

Table 2.29b. Viscosity (kinematic) or thermal diffusity interconversion factors

from \ to	$m^2\ s^{-1}$	St	$m^2\ h^{-1}$	$ft^2\ s^{-1}$	$ft^2\ h^{-1}$
1 meter squared per second ($m^2\ s^{-1}$)	1.0	1.0×10^4	3.6×10^3	10.7639	$3.875\,01 \times 10^4$
1 stokes (St)	1.0×10^{-4}	1.0	0.360	$1.076\,39 \times 10^{-3}$	3.875 01
1 meter squared per hour ($m^2\ h^{-1}$)	$2.777\,78 \times 10^{-4}$	2.777 78	1.0	$2.989\,98 \times 10^{-3}$	10.763 93
1 foot squared per second ($ft^2\ s^{-1}$)	0.092 903 0	929.030	334.451	1.0	3.6×10^3
1 foot squared per hour ($ft^2\ h^{-1}$)	$2.580\,64 \times 10^{-5}$	0.258 064	0.092 903	$2.777\,78 \times 10^{-4}$	1.0

2.30 Surface tension ($N\ m^{-1}$)

The surface tension is the ratio between the force across a line element in a surface and the length of the line element. The SI unit for surface tension is newton per meter ($N\ m^{-1}$), which is equivalent to joule per meter squared ($J\ m^{-2}$).

The commonly used units and their conversion factors to $N\ m^{-1}$ (SI unit) are listed in Table 2.30a. The various interconversion factors for the units of surface tension are presented in Table 2.30b.

Table 2.30a. Miscellaneous units of surface tension

Unit	$N\ m^{-1}$
1 dyne per centimeter ($dyn\ cm^{-1}$)	1.0×10^{-3}
1 erg per centimeter squared ($erg\ cm^{-2}$)	1.0×10^{-3}
1 erg per millimeter squared ($erg\ mm^{-2}$)	0.1
1 gram per centimeter ($g\ cm^{-1}$)	0.980 665
1 kilogram-force per meter (kilopond per meter) ($kgf\ m^{-1}$)	9.806 65
1 milligram per inch ($mg\ in^{-1}$)	$3.860\ 855 \times 10^{-4}$
1 milligram per millimeter ($mg\ mm^{-1}$)	$9.806\ 65 \times 10^{-3}$
1 millinewton per meter ($mN\ m^{-1}$)	1.0×10^{-3}
1 newton per meter ($N\ m^{-1}$)	1.0
1 poundal per inch ($pdl\ in^{-1}$)	5.443 108 5

Table 2.30b. Surface tension interconversion factors

from \ to	$N\ m^{-1}$	$mN\ m^{-1}$	$kgf\ m^{-1}$	$dyn\ cm^{-1}$	$pdl\ in^{-1}$
1 newton per meter (= $1\ kg\ s^{-2}$) ($N\ m^{-1}$)	1.0	1.0×10^{3}	0.102	1.0×10^{3}	0.183 718 5
1 millinewton per meter ($mN\ m^{-1}$)	1.0×10^{-3}	1.0	1.02×10^{-4}	1.0	$1.837\ 185 \times 10^{-4}$
1 kilogram-force per meter (= $1\ kp\ m^{-1}$) ($kgf\ m^{-1}$)	9.807	9.807×10^{3}	1.0	9.807×10^{3}	1.801 727
1 dyne per centimeter (= $1\ erg\ cm^{-2}$) ($dyn\ cm^{-1}$)	1.0×10^{-3}	1.0	1.02×10^{-4}	1.0	$1.837\ 185 \times 10^{-4}$
1 poundal per inch ($pdl\ in^{-1}$)	5.443 108 5	$5.443\ 108 \times 10^{3}$	0.555 023	$5.443\ 108 \times 10^{3}$	1.0

2.31 Temperature (K)

There are five different units of temperature

degree Celsius (or centigrade) (°C)
degree Fahrenheit (°F)
degree Rankine (°R)
degree Réaumur (°r)
degree Kelvin (K)

The formulas giving the interrelationships among the various units of temperature are given in Table 2.31a. The interconversion factors for the units of temperature interval (difference) are given in Table 2.31b.

The degree values of the five scales are in accordance with the relationship

$$5\ \text{K} = 5°\text{C} = 9°\text{F} = 9°\text{R} = 4°\text{r}$$

Table 2.31a. Temperature interconversion factors

from \ to	°C	°F	K	°R	°r
degree Celsius (°C)	1.0	$\frac{5}{9}$ (°F − 32)	K − 273.15	$\frac{5}{9}$ (°R − 491.67)	$\frac{5}{4}$ °r
degree Farenheit (°F)	$\frac{9}{5}$ °C + 32	1.0	$\frac{9}{5}$ K − 459.67	°R − 459.67	$\frac{9}{4}$ °r + 32
degree Kelvin (K)	°C + 273.15	$\frac{5}{9}$ °F + 459.67	1.0	$\frac{5}{9}$ °R	$\frac{5}{4}$ °r + 273.15
degree Rankine (°R)	$\frac{9}{5}$ °C + 491.67	°F + 459.67	$\frac{9}{5}$ K	1.0	$\frac{9}{4}$ °r + 491.67
degree Réaumur (°r)	$\frac{4}{5}$ °C	$\frac{4}{9}$ °F − 32	$\frac{4}{5}$ K − 273.15	$\frac{4}{9}$ °R − 491.67	1.0

Table 2.31b. Temperature interval interconversion factors

from \ to	°C or K	°F or °R	°r
1°C = 1 K	1.0	$\frac{9}{5}$	$\frac{4}{5}$
1°F = 1°R	$\frac{5}{9}$	1.0	$\frac{4}{9}$
1°r	$\frac{5}{4}$	$\frac{9}{4}$	1.0

2.32 Energy (work or heat) (J)

Energy is the product of force and distance. There are different types of energy (e.g., mechanical, electrical, kinetic, potential, radiant, etc.)

The unit of energy may be expressed in many ways. A list of the common units is presented in Table 2.32a. The interconversion factors for the units of energy are given in Table 2.32b.

Table 2.32a. Miscellaneous units for energy (work or heat)

Unit	J
1 British thermal unit (Btu)	
international	$1.055\,06 \times 10^3$
mean	$1.055\,75 \times 10^3$
	1.0558×10^3
1 British thermal unit	
15°C	$1.054\,73 \times 10^3$
39°F	$1.059\,67 \times 10^3$
60°F	1.0545×10^3
1 calorie (cal)	
I.T.	4.1868
mean	4.190 02
thermochemical	4.1840
1 calorie	
15°C	4.1855
20°C	4.1819
1 centigrade heat unit (CHU)	1.9004×10^3
1 cheval-vapeur-heure	$2.647\,795 \times 10^6$
1 cubic centimeter-atmosphere (cm^3 atm)	0.101 325
1 cubic foot-atmosphere (ft^3 atm)	$2.869\,20 \times 10^3$
1 cubic foot-(pound force per square inch)	195.2368
1 dyne-centimeter (dyn cm)	1.0×10^{-7}
1 electron volt	$1.602\,191\,7 \times 10^{-19}$
1 erg	1.0×10^{-7}
1 foot pound-force (ft lbf)	1.355 82
1 foot-poundal (ft pdl)	0.042 140 1
1 frigorie	-4.1855×10^3
1 gram-force centimeter (gf cm)	$9.806\,65 \times 10^{-5}$
1 horsepower-hour (hp h)	$2.684\,52 \times 10^6$
electric	2.6856×10^6
1 horsepower-year (hp yr)	306.4522
1 joule (J)	
absolute	1.0
international before 1948	1.000 19
1 kilocalorie (I.T.) (kcal)	4.1868×10^3
1 kilogram-force meter (kgf m)	9.806 65
1 kilopond-meter (Germany) (kp m)	9.806 65
1 kilowatt-hour (kW h)	3.6×10^6
1 liter-atmosphere (1 atm)	101.325
1 mass unit	$1.492\,092 \times 10^{-12}$
1 newton-meter (N m)	1.0
1 pascal cubic meter (Pa m^3)	1.0
1 pound-centigrade unit (p.c.u.)	$1.899\,108 \times 10^3$
1 pound of carbon to CO_2	1.5336×10^7
1 pound of water evaporated from (at 212°F)	1.0224×10^6
1 Rydberg unit of energy	$2.169\,367\,5 \times 10^{-18}$
1 therm	1.055×10^8
1 thermie (th)	4.1868×10^6
1 ton of refrig. (US standard)	$3.038\,318 \times 10^8$
1 tonne-calorie	4.1868×10^6
1 volt-coulomb (VC)	
absolute	1.0
international	1.000 165 027
1 watt-hour (W h)	
absolute	3.600×10^3
international	$3.600\,593\,38 \times 10^3$
1 watt-minute (absolute) (W min)	60.00
1 watt-second (W s)	
absolute	1.0
international	1.000 165 027

Table 2.32b. Energy (work) interconversion factors

from \ to	J	erg	cal_{IT}	$kcal_{IT}$	Btu	ft lbf	kWh	kgf m	hp h
1 absolute joule (= 1 W s) (J)	1.0	1.0×10^{7}	0.238 846	$2.388\,46 \times 10^{-4}$	$9.478\,17 \times 10^{-4}$	0.737 562	$2.777\,778 \times 10^{-7}$	0.101 971 6	$3.725\,061 \times 10^{-7}$
1 erg (= 1 dyn cm) (erg)	1.0×10^{-7}	1.0	$2.388\,46 \times 10^{-8}$	$2.388\,46 \times 10^{-11}$	$9.478\,17 \times 10^{-11}$	$7.375\,62 \times 10^{-8}$	$2.777\,78 \times 10^{-14}$	$1.019\,716 \times 10^{-8}$	$3.725\,061 \times 10^{-14}$
1 calorie (I.T.) (cal_{IT})	4.1868	4.1868×10^{7}	1.0	1.0×10^{-3}	$3.968\,32 \times 10^{-3}$	3.008 03	$1.162\,98 \times 10^{-6}$	0.426 928	$1.559\,61 \times 10^{-6}$
1 kilocalorie (I.T.) ($kcal_{IT}$)	4.1868×10^{3}	4.1868×10^{10}	1.0×10^{3}	1.0	3.968 32	$3.088\,03 \times 10^{3}$	$1.162\,98 \times 10^{-3}$	426.928	$1.559\,61 \times 10^{-3}$
1 British thermal unit (Btu)	$1.055\,06 \times 10^{3}$	$1.055\,06 \times 10^{10}$	251.996	0.251 996	1.0	778.169	$2.930\,71 \times 10^{-4}$	107.584	$3.930\,15 \times 10^{-4}$
1 foot pound-force (ft lbf)	1.355 82	$1.355\,82 \times 10^{7}$	0.323 832	$3.238\,32 \times 10^{-4}$	$1.285\,07 \times 10^{-3}$	1.0	$3.766\,16 \times 10^{-7}$	0.138 255	$5.050\,51 \times 10^{-7}$
1 kilowatt-hour (kWh)	3.6×10^{6}	3.6×10^{13}	8.5945×10^{5}	859.45	$3.412\,14 \times 10^{3}$	$2.655\,22 \times 10^{6}$	1.0	$3.670\,98 \times 10^{5}$	1.341 02
1 kilogram-force meter (kgf m)	9.806 65	$9.806\,65 \times 10^{7}$	2.342 32	$2.342\,32 \times 10^{-3}$	$9.295\,06 \times 10^{-3}$	7.233 011	$2.724\,07 \times 10^{-6}$	1.0	$3.653\,03 \times 10^{-6}$
1 horsepower hour (hp h)	$2.684\,52 \times 10^{6}$	$2.684\,52 \times 10^{13}$	$6.411\,86 \times 10^{5}$	641.186	$2.544\,43 \times 10^{3}$	1.98×10^{6}	0.745 701	$2.737\,45 \times 10^{5}$	1.0

2.33 Power (heat-flow rate) (J s^{-1})

The ratio between energy and time is the power.

The various units of power are summarized in Table 2.33a. The interconversion factors for the units are presented in Table 2.33b.

Table 2.33a. Miscellaneous units of power

Unit	J s^{-1}
1 British thermal unit per hour (Btu h^{-1})	0.293 071
1 British thermal unit per minute (Btu min^{-1})	17.584 26
1 British thermal unit per second (Btu s^{-1})	1.055 055 6 × 10^3
1 British thermal unit (mean) per minute	17.5978
1 calorie (I.T.) per hour (cal$_{IT}$ h^{-1})	1.1630 × 10^{-3}
1 calorie (I.T.) per minute (cal$_{IT}$ min^{-1})	0.069 78
1 calorie (I.T.) per second (cal$_{IT}$ s^{-1})	4.1868
1 calorie (mean) per hour	1.163 900 × 10^{-3}
1 calorie (mean) per minute	0.069 833 7
1 calorie (mean) per second	4.190 02
1 calorie (thermal) per hour	1.162 222 × 10^{-3}
1 calorie (thermal) per minute	0.069 733
1 calorie (thermal) per second	4.1840
1 cheval-vapeur	735.499
1 cubic centimeter-atmosphere per hour (cm^3 atm h^{-1})	2.814 583 × 10^{-5}
1 cubic foot-atmosphere per hour (ft^3 atm h^{-1})	0.797 003 3
1 dyne-centimeter per second (dyn cm s^{-1})	1.0 × 10^{-7}
1 erg per minute (erg min^{-1})	1.666 667 × 10^{-9}
1 erg per second (erg s^{-1})	1.0 × 10^{-7}
1 foot pound-force per hour (ft lbf h^{-1})	3.766 17 × 10^{-4}
1 foot pound-force per minute (ft lbf min^{-1})	0.022 597
1 foot pound-force per second (ft lbf s^{-1})	1.355 82
1 foot-poundal per minute (ft pdl min^{-1})	7.023 359 6 × 10^{-4}
1 force de cheval	735.499
1 gram-force centimeter per second (gf cm s^{-1})	9.806 652 × 10^{-5}
1 hectowatt (hW)	100.0
1 horsepower (hp)	
boiler	9.809 50 × 10^3
electric	746.00
imperial	745.70
metric	735.499
water	746.043
1 joule per hour (J h^{-1})	2.777 778 × 10^{-4}
1 joule per minute (J min^{-1})	0.016 666 67
1 joule per second (J s^{-1})	1.0
1 kilocalorie (I.T.) per hour (kcal$_{IT}$ h^{-1})	1.1630
1 kilocalorie (I.T.) per minute (kcal$_{IT}$ min^{-1})	69.78
1 kilocalorie (I.T.) per second (kcal$_{IT}$ s^{-1})	4.1868 × 10^3
1 kilogram-force meter per hour (kgf m h^{-1})	2.724 068 2 × 10^{-3}
1 kilogram-force meter per minute (kgf m min^{-1})	0.163 444 17
1 kilogram-force meter per second (kgf m s^{-1})	9.806 65
1 kilowatt (kW)	1.0 × 10^3
1 kilowatt (international before 1948)	1.000 165 × 10^3
1 liter-atmosphere per hour (1 atm h^{-1})	0.028 146 655
1 ton of refrigeration	3.516 85 × 10^3
1 watt (W)	1.0
1 watt (international)	1.000 165

Table 2.33b. Power (heat-flow rate) interconversion factors

from \ to	W	kgf m s^{-1}	hp (metric)	hp (imperial)	erg s^{-1}	ft lbf s^{-1}	$kcal_{IT}$ h^{-1}	Btu h^{-1}
1 watt (= 1 J s^{-1}) (W)	1.0	0.101 971 6	$1.359\ 62 \times 10^{-3}$	$1.341\ 02 \times 10^{-3}$	1.0×10^{7}	0.737 562	0.859 845	3.412 14
1 kilogram-force meter per second (kgf m s^{-1})	9.806 65	1.0	0.013 333 3	0.013 150 93	$9.806\ 65 \times 10^{7}$	7.233 014	8.432 20	33.4617
1 horsepower (metric) (hp_m)	735.499	75.0	1.0	0.986 320 1	$7.354\ 99 \times 10^{9}$	542.476	632.415	$2.509\ 63 \times 10^{3}$
1 horsepower (imperial) (hp_{imp})	745.70	76.040 22	1.013 87	1.0	7.4570×10^{9}	550.0	641.186	$2.544\ 43 \times 10^{3}$
1 erg per second (erg s^{-1})	1.0×10^{-7}	$1.019\ 716 \times 10^{-8}$	$1.359\ 62 \times 10^{-10}$	$1.341\ 02 \times 10^{-10}$	1.0	$7.375\ 62 \times 10^{-8}$	$8.598\ 45 \times 10^{-8}$	$3.412\ 14 \times 10^{-7}$
1 foot pound-force per second (ft lbf s^{-1})	1.355 82	0.138 254 95	$1.843\ 399 \times 10^{-3}$	$1.818\ 182 \times 10^{-3}$	$1.355\ 82 \times 10^{7}$	1.0	1.165 79	4.626 24
1 kilocalorie (I.T.) per hour ($kcal_{IT}$ h^{-1})	1.162 98	0.118 593	$1.581\ 24 \times 10^{-3}$	$1.559\ 61 \times 10^{-3}$	$1.162\ 98 \times 10^{7}$	0.857 785	1.0	3.968 32
1 British thermal unit per hour (Btu h^{-1})	0.293 071	0.029 884 9	$3.984\ 66 \times 10^{-4}$	$3.930\ 15 \times 10^{-4}$	$2.930\ 71 \times 10^{6}$	0.216 158	0.251 996	1.0

2.34 Specific energy (calorific value or enthalpy) (J kg^{-1})

Specific energy is the ratio between energy and mass. Specific energy may be expressed in several units (*see* Table 2.34a). Molecular energy may be derived by expressing the mass in molar quantity. The interconversion factors between the units of specific energy are given in Table 2.34b and molecular energy in Table 2.34c.

Some useful expressions are:

$$1 \text{ Amagat unit of P V} = 528.783 \text{ cal mol}^{-1} = 2.213\,908\,7 \times 10^{3} \text{ J mol}^{-1}$$

$$1 \text{ eV mol}^{-1} = 9.648\,676 \times 10^{4} \text{ J mol}^{-1}$$

Table 2.34a. Miscellaneous units of specific energy

Unit	J kg^{-1}
1 British thermal unit per pound (Btu lb^{-1})	2.326×10^{3}
1 British thermal unit (International Steam Table) per pound	$2.324\,48 \times 10^{3}$
1 British thermal unit (mean) per pound	$2.327\,79 \times 10^{3}$
1 calorie (I.T.) per gram (cal$_{IT}$ g $^{-1}$)	4.1868×10^{3}
1 calorie (mean) per gram	$4.190\,02 \times 10^{3}$
1 calorie (thermal) per gram	4.1840×10^{3}
1 centigrade heat unit per pound (Chu lb^{-1})	4.1868×10^{3}
1 cubic centimeter-atmosphere per gram (cm^3 atm g^{-1})	$1.013\,25 \times 10^{-4}$
1 cubic foot-atmosphere per pound (ft^3 atm lb^{-1})	$6.325\,510\,8 \times 10^{3}$
1 cubic foot-(pound per square inch) per pound	430.425 45
1 foot pound-force per pound (ft lbf lb^{-1})	2.989 07
1 horsepower-hour per pound (hp h lb^{-1})	$5.918\,35 \times 10^{6}$
1 joule per gram (J g^{-1})	1.0×10^{3}
1 joule per kilogram (J kg^{-1})	1.0
1 kilocalorie (I.T.) per gram (kcal$_{IT}$ g^{-1})	4.1868
1 kilocalorie (I.T.) per kilogram (kcal$_{IT}$ kg^{-1})	4.1868×10^{3}
1 kilocalorie (thermal) per kilogram	4.1840×10^{3}
1 kilocalorie (15°C) per kilogram	4.1855×10^{3}
1 kilogram-force meter per gram (kgf m g^{-1})	$9.806\,65 \times 10^{3}$
1 kilogram-force meter per kilogram (kgf m kg^{-1})	9.806 65
1 kilowatt-hour per gram (kWh g^{-1})	3.6×10^{9}
1 kilowatt-hour per pound (kWh lb^{-1})	$7.936\,648 \times 10^{6}$
1 pound-centigrade unit per pound (p.c.u. lb^{-1})	4.1868×10^{3}
1 rad (radiation dose absorbed)	0.01

Table 2.34b. Specific energy (enthalpy) interconversion factors

from \ to	$J\ kg^{-1}$	$ft\ lbf\ lb^{-1}$	$kgf\ m\ kg^{-1}$	$Btu\ lb^{-1}$	$kcal_{IT}\ kg^{-1}$	$cal_{IT}\ g^{-1}$
1 joule per kilogram ($J\ kg^{-1}$)	1.0	0.334 553	0.101 972	$4.299\ 23 \times 10^{-4}$	$2.388\ 46 \times 10^{-4}$	$2.388\ 46 \times 10^{-4}$
1 foot pound-force per pound ($ft\ lbf\ lb^{-1}$)	2.989 07	1.0	0.3048	$1.285\ 07 \times 10^{-3}$	$7.139\ 26 \times 10^{-4}$	$7.139\ 26 \times 10^{-4}$
1 kilogram-force meter per kilogram ($kgf\ m\ kg^{-1}$)	9.806 65	3.280 84	1.0	4.2161×10^{-3}	$2.342\ 28 \times 10^{-3}$	$2.342\ 28 \times 10^{-3}$
1 British thermal unit per pound ($Btu\ lb^{-1}$)	2.326×10^{3}	778.169	237.186	1.0	0.555 556	0.555 556
1 kilocalorie (I.T.) per kilogram ($kcal_{IT}\ kg^{-1}$)	4.1868×10^{3}	1.4007×10^{3}	426.935	1.80	1.0	1.0
1 calorie (I.T.) per gram ($cal_{IT}\ g^{-1}$)	4.1868×10^{3}	1.4007×10^{3}	426.935	1.80	1.0	1.0

1 chu lb^{-1} = 1 kcal kg^{-1} = 1 cal g^{-1}

Table 2.34c. Molecular energy interconversion factors

from \ to	$J\ mol^{-1}$	$cal\ mol^{-1}$	$cm^3\ atm\ mol^{-1}$	$kWh\ mol^{-1}$	$Btu\ lb\text{-}mol^{-1}$	$cm^{-1}\ molecule^{-1}$	$eV\ molecule^{-1}$
1 joule per mole ($J\ mol^{-1}$)	1.0	0.238 846	9.869 23	$2.777\ 78 \times 10^{-7}$	0.429 922 6	0.083 594 0	$1.036\ 411\ 6 \times 10^{-5}$
1 calorie per mole ($cal\ mol^{-1}$)	4.1868	1.0	41.320 48	$1.162\ 999 \times 10^{-6}$	1.799 999 8	0.350 133 3	$4.339\ 246\ 0 \times 10^{-5}$
1 cubic centimeter-atmosphere per mole ($cm^3\ atm\ mol^{-1}$)	0.101 325	0.024 201 07	1.0	$2.814\ 582 \times 10^{-8}$	0.043 561 98	$8.470\ 165 \times 10^{-3}$	$1.050\ 141 \times 10^{-6}$
1 kilowatt-hour per mole ($kWh\ mol^{-1}$)	3.6×10^{6}	$8.598\ 46 \times 10^{5}$	$3.552\ 925 \times 10^{7}$	1.0	$1.547\ 243 \times 10^{6}$	$3.009\ 386 \times 10^{5}$	37.310 79
1 British thermal unit per pound-mole ($Btu\ lb\text{-}mol^{-1}$)	2.3620	0.555 555 6	22.9558	$6.461\ 098\ 9 \times 10^{-7}$	1.0	0.194 439 6	$2.410\ 698 \times 10^{-5}$
1 reciprocal centimeter-molecule ($cm^{-1}\ molecule^{-1}$)	11.962 58	2.857 214	118.0614	$3.322\ 937 \times 10^{-6}$	5.142 990 4	1.0	$1.239\ 813 \times 10^{-4}$
1 electron volt per molecule ($eV\ molecule^{-1}$)	$9.648\ 676 \times 10^{4}$	$2.304\ 548 \times 10^{4}$	$9.522\ 503\ 0 \times 10^{5}$	0.026 801 868	$4.148\ 190\ 6 \times 10^{4}$	$8.065\ 73 \times 10^{3}$	1.0

2.35 Heat per unit volume (J m^{-3})

The heat per unit volume may be expressed in several common units (*see* Table 2.35a). The interconversion factors for the units are presented in Table 2.35b.

Table 2.35a. Miscellaneous units of heat per unit volume

Unit	J m^{-3}
1 British thermal unit per cubic foot (Btu ft^{-3})	$3.725\,89 \times 10^4$
1 joule per cubic meter (J m^{-3})	1.0
1 kilocalorie (I.T.) per cubic meter (kcal$_{IT}$ m^{-3})	4.1868×10^3
1 kilocalorie (thermal) per cubic meter (kcal$_{th}$ m^{-3})	4.184×10^3
1 kilocalorie (15°C) per cubic meter	4.1855×10^3
1 therm per cubic foot	1.055×10^8
1 therm per gallon (UK)	2.3208×10^{10}
1 thermie per liter (th l^{-1})	4.1855×10^9

Table 2.35b. Heat per unit volume interconversion factors

from \ to	$J\ m^{-3}$	$cal_{IT}\ m^{-3}$	$kcal_{IT}\ m^{-3}$	$Btu\ ft^{-3}$	$th\ l^{-1}$	therm gal $(UK)^{-1}$
1 joule per cubic meter ($J\ m^{-3}$)	1.0	0.238 846	$2.388\ 46 \times 10^{-4}$	$2.683\ 92 \times 10^{-5}$	2.3892×10^{-10}	$4.308\ 86 \times 10^{-11}$
1 calorie (I.T.) per cubic meter ($cal_{IT}\ m^{-3}$)	4.1868	1.0	1.0×10^{-3}	1.1237×10^{-4}	$1.000\ 31 \times 10^{-9}$	1.8404×10^{-10}
1 kilocalorie (I.T.) per cubic meter ($kcal_{IT}\ m^{-3}$)	4.1868×10^{3}	1.0×10^{3}	1.0	0.112 37	$1.000\ 31 \times 10^{-6}$	$1.840\ 4 \times 10^{-7}$
1 British thermal unit per cubic foot ($Btu\ ft^{-3}$)	$3.725\ 89 \times 10^{4}$	$8.899\ 15 \times 10^{3}$	8.899 15	1.0	$8.901\ 91 \times 10^{-6}$	$1.605\ 44 \times 10^{-6}$
1 thermie per liter ($th\ l^{-1}$)	4.1855×10^{9}	$9.996\ 90 \times 10^{8}$	$9.996\ 90 \times 10^{5}$	$1.123\ 354\ 4 \times 10^{5}$	1.0	0.180 347
1 therm per gallon (UK) (therm gal $(UK)^{-1}$)	$2.320\ 80 \times 10^{10}$	$5.543\ 13 \times 10^{9}$	$5.543\ 13 \times 10^{6}$	$6.228\ 83 \times 10^{5}$	5.544 85	1.0

2.36 Specific heat capacity (specific entropy) (J kg^{-1} K^{-1})

Specific heat capacity is the ratio between the heat and the product of mass and temperature interval.

The various units used to express specific heat capacity are summarized in Table 2.36a. The interconversion factors for the units are presented in Table 2.36b. The heat capacity may be expressed in molar units (*see* Table 2.36c). The heat capacity may also be expressed on volumetric basis, that is the ratio between the heat and the product of volume and temperature interval. Similarly to the specific heat capacity on the mass basis, the units of heat capacity on volume basis are tabulated in Tables 2.36d and 2.36e.

Some simple equalities are useful to remember

$$1 \text{ cal}_{IT}\text{ g}^{-1}\text{ °C}^{-1} = 1 \text{ kcal}_{IT}\text{ kg}^{-1}\text{ °C}^{-1}$$

$$= 1 \text{ Chu lb}^{-1}\text{ °C}^{-1} = 1 \text{ Btu lb}^{-1}\text{ °F}^{-1}$$

$$= 4.1868 \times 10^3 \text{ J kg}^{-1}\text{ °C}^{-1}$$

$$1 \text{ cal}_{IT}\text{ g}^{-1}\text{ K}^{-1} = 1 \text{ kcal}_{IT}\text{ kg}^{-1}\text{ K}^{-1} = 1 \text{ Chu lb}^{-1}\text{ K}^{-1}$$

$$= 1 \text{ Btu lb}^{-1}\text{ °R}^{-1}$$

$$= 4.1868 \times 10^3 \text{ J kg}^{-1}\text{ K}^{-1}$$

Table 2.36a. Miscellaneous units of specific heat capacity

Unit	J kg^{-1} K^{-1}
1 British thermal unit per pound degree Celsius (Btu lb^{-1} °C^{-1})	7.536 24 × 10^3
1 British thermal unit per pound degree Fahrenheit (Btu lb^{-1} °F^{-1})	4.1868 × 10^3
1 calorie (I.T.) per gram degree Kelvin (cal$_{IT}$ g^{-1} K^{-1})	4.1868 × 10^3
1 calorie (thermal) per gram degree Celsius (cal g^{-1} °C^{-1})	4.1840 × 10^3
1 celsius heat unit per pound degree Celsius (Chu lb^{-1} °C^{-1})	4.1868 × 10^3
1 centigrade heat unit per pound degree Celsius (Chu lb^{-1} °C^{-1})	4.1868 × 10^3
1 foot pound-force per pound degree Fahrenheit (ft lbf lb^{-1} °F^{-1})	5.380 32
1 joule per gram degree Kelvin (J g^{-1} K^{-1})	1.0 × 10^3
1 joule per kilogram degree Celsius (J kg^{-1} °C^{-1})	1.0
1 joule per kilogram degree Kelvin (J kg^{-1} K^{-1})	1.0
1 kilocalorie (I.T) per kilogram degree Kelvin (kcal$_{IT}$ kg^{-1} K^{-1})	4.1868 × 10^3
1 kilocalorie (thermal) per kilogram degree Kelvin (kcal kg^{-1} K^{-1})	4.1840 × 10^3
1 kilocalorie (15°C) per kilogram degree Kelvin	4.1855 × 10^3
1 kilogram-force meter per kilogram degree Kelvin (kgf m kg^{-1} K^{-1})	9.806 65
1 pound-centigrade unit per pound degree Celsius (p.c.u. lb^{-1} °C^{-1})	4.1868 × 10^3

Table 2.36b. Specific heat capacity (specific entropy) interconversion factors

from \ to	$J\ kg^{-1}\ K^{-1}$	$cal_{IT}\ kg^{-1}\ K^{-1}$	$ft\ lbf\ lb^{-1}\ {}^{\circ}F^{-1}$	$kgf\ m\ kg^{-1}\ K^{-1}$	$Btu\ lb^{-1}\ {}^{\circ}F^{-1}$ or $kcal_{IT}\ kg^{-1}\ K^{-1}$
1 joule per kilogram degree Kelvin ($J\ kg^{-1}\ K^{-1}$)	1.0	0.238 846	0.185 863	0.101 971 6	$2.388\ 459 \times 10^{-4}$
1 calorie (I.T.) per kilogram degree Kelvin ($cal_{IT}\ kg^{-1}\ K^{-1}$)	4.1868	1.0	0.778 169	0.426 935	1.0×10^{-3}
1 foot pound-force per pound degree Fahrenheit ($ft\ lbf\ lb^{-1}\ {}^{\circ}F^{-1}$)	5.380 32	1.285 07	1.0	0.548 64	$1.285\ 07 \times 10^{-3}$
1 kilogram-force meter per kilogram degree Kelvin ($kgf\ m\ kg^{-1}\ K^{-1}$)	9.806 65	2.342 28	1.822 69	1.0	$2.342\ 28 \times 10^{-3}$
1 kilocalorie (I.T.) per kilogram degree Kelvin or British thermal unit per pound degree Fahrenheit ($kcal_{IT}\ kg^{-1}\ K^{-1}$ or 1 $Btu\ lb^{-1}\ {}^{\circ}F^{-1}$)	4.1868×10^{3}	1.0×10^{3}	778.169	426.935	1.0

Table 2.36c. Miscellaneous units of molar heat capacity

Unit	$J\ mol^{-1}\ K^{-1}$
1 calorie (I.T.) per mole degree Kelvin ($cal_{IT}\ mol^{-1}\ K^{-1}$)	4.1868
1 Clausius (joule per mole degree Kelvin)	1.0
1 entropy unit (EU or eu)	4.1868
1 gibbs per mole (gib mol^{-1})	4.1868
1 joule per mole degree Kelvin ($J\ mol^{-1}\ K^{-1}$)	1.0
1 Thomson (calorie per mole degree Kelvin)	4.1868

Table 2.36d. Miscellaneous units of heat capacity on volumetric basis

Unit	$J\ m^{-3}\ K^{-1}$
1 British thermal unit per cubic foot degree Fahrenheit (Btu $ft^{-3}\,°F^{-1}$)	$6.706\,61 \times 10^4$
1 calorie (I.T.) per liter degree Celsius ($cal_{IT}\ l^{-1}\ °C^{-1}$)	4.1868×10^3
1 joule per cubic centimeter degree Celsius ($J\ cm^{-3}\ °C^{-1}$)	1.0×10^6
1 joule per cubic meter degree Kelvin ($J\ m^{-3}\ K^{-1}$)	1.0
1 kilocalorie (I.T.) per cubic meter degree Kelvin ($kcal_{IT}\ m^{-3}\ K^{-1}$)	4.1868×10^3
1 kilocalorie (thermal) per cubic meter degree Kelvin ($kcal\ m^{-3}\ K^{-1}$)	4.1840×10^3
1 kilocalorie (15°C) per cubic meter degree Kelvin	4.1855×10^3

Table 2.36e. Heat capacity on volumetric basis interconversion factors

from \ to	$J\ m^{-3}\ K^{-1}$	$cal_{IT}\ l^{-1}\ °C^{-1}$	$kcal_{IT}\ m^{-3}\ K^{-1}$	$Btu\ ft^{-3}\ °F^{-1}$	$J\ cm^{-3}\ °C^{-1}$
1 joule per cubic meter degree Kelvin ($J\ m^{-3}\ K^{-1}$)	1.0	$2.388\,53 \times 10^{-4}$	$2.388\,46 \times 10^{-4}$	$1.491\,07 \times 10^{-5}$	1.0×10^{-6}
1 calorie (I.T.) per liter degree Celsius ($cal_{IT}\ l^{-1}\ °C^{-1}$)	$4.186\,68 \times 10^{3}$	1.0	0.999 972	0.062 426 3	$4.186\,68 \times 10^{-3}$
1 kilocalorie (I.T.) per cubic meter degree Kelvin ($kcal_{IT}\ m^{-3}\ K^{-1}$)	4.1868×10^{3}	1.000 028	1.0	0.062 428 0	4.1868×10^{-3}
1 British thermal unit per cubic foot degree Fahrenheit ($Btu\ ft^{-3}\ °F^{-1}$)	$6.706\,61 \times 10^{4}$	16.0189	16.0185	1.0	0.067 066 1
1 joule per cubic meter degree Celsius ($J\ cm^{-3}\ °C^{-1}$)	1.0×10^{6}	238.853	238.846	14.9107	1.0

2.37 Heat flux density (heat losses from surface) (W m^{-2})

Heat flux density is the ratio between the heat and the product of area and time.

The units of the heat flux density may be expressed in several ways (*see* Table 2.37a). The interconversion factors for the units are presented in Table 2.37b.

Table 2.37a. Miscellaneous units for heat flux density

Unit	W m^{-2}
1 British thermal unit per square foot hour (Btu ft^{-2} h^{-1})	3.154 59
1 British thermal unit per square foot minute (Btu ft^{-2} min^{-1})	189.276 27
1 British thermal unit per square foot second (Btu ft^{-2} s^{-1})	1.135 652 4 × 10^4
1 calorie (I.T.) per square centimeter second (cal$_{IT}$ cm^{-2} s^{-1})	4.186 80 x 10^4
1 calorie (thermal) per square centimeter second (cal$_{th}$ cm^{-2} s^{-1})	4.1840 × 10^4
1 foot pound per square foot minute (ft lb ft^{-2} min^{-1})	0.243 231 48
1 horsepower (metric) per square foot (hp$_m$ ft^{-2})	7.916 849 × 10^3
1 kilocalorie (I.T.) per square meter hour (kcal$_{IT}$ m^{-2} h^{-1})	1.163
1 kilowatt per square foot (kW ft^{-2})	1.076 391 5 × 10^4
1 watt per square centimeter (W cm^{-2})	1.0 × 10^4
1 watt per square inch (W in^{-2})	1.550 × 10^3
1 watt per square meter (W m^{-2})	1.0

Table 2.37b. Heat flux density (heat losses from surface) interconversion factors

from \ to	$W\ m^{-2}$	$W\ cm^{-2}$	$W\ in^{-2}$	$cal_{IT}\ cm^{-2}\ s^{-1}$	$kcal_{IT}\ m^{-2}\ h^{-1}$	$Btu\ ft^{-2}\ h^{-1}$	$Btu\ ft^{-2}\ s^{-1}$
1 watt per square meter ($W\ m^{-2}$)	1.0	1.0×10^{-4}	6.4516×10^{-4}	$2.388\ 46 \times 10^{-5}$	0.859 845	0.316 998	$8.805\ 51 \times 10^{-5}$
1 watt per square centimeter ($W\ cm^{-2}$)	1.0×10^{4}	1.0	6.4516	0.238 846	$8.598\ 45 \times 10^{3}$	$3.169\ 98 \times 10^{3}$	0.880 551
1 watt per square inch ($W\ in^{-2}$)	1.55×10^{3}	0.1550	1.0	0.037 021 2	$1.332\ 76 \times 10^{3}$	491.348	0.136 485
1 calorie (I.T.) per square centimeter second ($cal_{IT}\ cm^{-2}\ s^{-1}$)	4.1868×10^{4}	4.1868	27.0116	1.0	3.6×10^{4}	$1.327\ 21 \times 10^{4}$	3.686 694
1 kilocalorie (I.T.) per square meter hour ($kcal_{IT}\ m^{-2}\ h^{-1}$)	1.163	1.163×10^{-4}	$7.503\ 21 \times 10^{-4}$	$2.777\ 78 \times 10^{-5}$	1.0	0.368 669	$1.024\ 081 \times 10^{-4}$
1 British thermal unit per square foot hour ($Btu\ ft^{-2}\ h^{-1}$)	3.154 59	$3.154\ 59 \times 10^{-4}$	$2.035\ 22 \times 10^{-3}$	$7.534\ 61 \times 10^{-5}$	2.712 46	1.0	$2.777\ 78 \times 10^{-4}$
1 British thermal unit per square foot second ($Btu\ ft^{-2}\ s^{-1}$)	$1.135\ 652 \times 10^{4}$	1.135 652	7.326 81	0.271 247	$9.764\ 881 \times 10^{3}$	3.6×10^{3}	1.0

2.38 Thermal conductivity ($W\ m^{-1}\ K^{-1}$)

The thermal conductivity (inverse of the thermal resistivity) is the ratio between the heat and the product of length, time and temperature difference.

The various units used in the technical literature are listed in Table 2.38a. The interconversion factors for the units of thermal conductivity are given in Table 2.38b.

Table 2.38a. Miscellaneous units of thermal conductivity

Unit	$W\ m^{-1}\ K^{-1}$
1 British thermal unit inch per foot squared hour degree Fahrenheit (Btu in $ft^{-2}\ h^{-1}\ °F^{-1}$)	0.144 228
1 British thermal unit per foot hour degree Fahrenheit (Btu $ft^{-1}\ h^{-1}\ °F^{-1}$)	1.730 73
1 British thermal unit per foot second degree Fahrenheit (Btu $ft^{-1}\ s^{-1}\ °F^{-1}$)	$6.230\ 64 \times 10^3$
1 British thermal unit per inch hour degree Fahrenheit (Btu $in^{-1}\ h^{-1}\ °F^{-1}$)	20.7688
1 calorie (I.T.) per centimeter second degree Celsius ($cal_{IT}\ cm^{-1}\ s^{-1}\ °C^{-1}$)	418.68
1 centigrade heat unit inch per foot squared hour degree Celsius (Chu in $ft^{-2}\ h^{-1}\ °C^{-1}$)	0.144 228
1 centigrade heat unit per foot hour degree Celsius (Chu $ft^{-1}\ h^{-1}\ °C^{-1}$)	1.730 73
1 joule per centimeter second degree Celsius ($J\ cm^{-1}\ s^{-1}\ °C^{-1}$)	100.0
1 kilocalorie per meter hour degree Celsius ($kcal_{IT}\ m^{-1}\ h^{-1}\ °C^{-1}$)	1.1630
1 kiloerg per centimeter second degree Celsius ($kerg\ cm^{-1}\ s^{-1}\ °C^{-1}$)	0.600
1 watt per centimeter degree Kelvin ($W\ cm^{-1}\ K^{-1}$)	100.0
1 watt per meter degree Celsius ($W\ m^{-1}\ °C^{-1}$)	1.0
1 watt per meter degree Kelvin ($W\ m^{-1}\ K^{-1}$)	1.0

Table 2.38b. Thermal conductivity interconversion factors

from \ to	$W\ m^{-1}\ °C^{-1}$	$W\ cm^{-1}\ °C^{-1}$	$cal_{IT}\ cm^{-1}\ s^{-1}\ °C^{-1}$	$kcal_{IT}\ m^{-1}\ h^{-1}\ °C^{-1}$	$Btu\ ft^{-1}\ s^{-1}\ °F^{-1}$	$Btu\ ft^{-1}\ h^{-1}\ °F^{-1}$	$Btu\ in^{-1}\ h^{-1}\ °F^{-1}$	$Btu\ in\ ft^{-2}\ h^{-1}\ °F^{-1}$
1 watt per meter degree ($W\ m^{-1}\ °C^{-1}$)	1.0	0.01	$2.388\ 46 \times 10^{-3}$	0.859 845	$1.604\ 97 \times 10^{-4}$	0.577 789	0.048 149 1	6.933 47
1 watt per centimeter degree Celsius ($W\ cm^{-1}\ °C^{-1}$)	100.0	1.0	0.238 846	85.9845	0.016 049 7	57.7789	4.814 91	693.347
1 calorie (I.T.) per centimeter second degree Celsius ($cal_{IT}\ cm^{-1}\ s^{-1}\ °C^{-1}$)	418.68	4.1868	1.0	360.0	0.067 196 9	241.909	20.1591	$2.902\ 91 \times 10^{3}$
1 kilocalorie (I.T.) per meter hour degree Celsius ($kcal_{IT}\ m^{-1}\ h^{-1}\ °C^{-1}$)	1.163	0.0163	$2.777\ 788 \times 10^{-3}$	1.0	$1.866\ 58 \times 10^{-4}$	0.671 969	0.055 997 4	8.063 63
1 British thermal unit per foot second degree Fahrenheit ($Btu\ ft^{-1}\ s^{-1}\ °F^{-1}$)	$6.230\ 64 \times 10^{3}$	62.3064	14.8816	$5.357\ 39 \times 10^{3}$	1.0	$3.6.\times 10^{3}$	300.0	4.32×10^{4}
1 British thermal unit per foot hour degree Fahrenheit ($Btu\ ft^{-1}\ h^{-1}\ °F^{-1}$)	1.730 73	0.017 307 3	$4.133\ 79 \times 10^{-3}$	1.488 16	$2.777\ 777\ 8 \times 10^{-4}$	1.0	0.083 333 33	12.0
1 British thermal unit per inch hour degree Fahrenheit ($Btu\ in^{-1}\ h^{-1}\ °F^{-1}$)	20.7688	0.207 688	0.049 605 4	17.858	$3.333\ 333\ 3 \times 10^{-3}$	12.0	1.0	144.0
1 British thermal unit inch per foot squared degree Fahrenheit ($Btu\ in\ ft^{-2}\ h^{-1}\ °F^{-1}$)	0.144 228	$1.442\ 28 \times 10^{-3}$	$3.444\ 82 \times 10^{-4}$	0.124 014	$2.314\ 81 \times 10^{-5}$	0.083 333 33	$6.944\ 444\ 4 \times 10^{-3}$	1.0

1 Chu $ft^{-1}\ h^{-1}\ °C^{-1}$ = 1 Btu $ft^{-1}\ h^{-1}\ °F^{-1}$
1 Chu in $ft^{-1}\ h^{-1}\ °C^{-1}$ 1 1 Btu in $ft^{-2}\ h^{-1}\ °F^{-1}$

2.39 Thermal conductance (heat transfer coefficient) ($W\ m^{-2}\ K^{-1}$)

The heat transfer coefficient or thermal conductance is the ratio between the heat and the product of area, time and temperature difference.

The different units for thermal conductance are summarized in Table 2.39a. The interconversion factors for the units are presented in Table 2.39b.

Table 2.39a. Miscellaneous units for thermal conductance

Unit	$W\ m^{-2}\ K^{-1}$
1 British thermal unit per square foot hour degree Fahrenheit ($Btu\ ft^{-2}\ h^{-1}\ {}^{\circ}F^{-1}$)	5.678 26
1 British thermal unit per square foot second degree Fahrenheit ($Btu\ ft^{-2}\ s^{-1}\ {}^{\circ}F^{-1}$)	$2.044\ 17 \times 10^4$
1 calorie (I.T.) per square centimeter second degree Kelvin ($cal_{IT}\ cm^{-2}\ s^{-1}\ K^{-1}$)	4.1868×10^4
1 calorie (thermal) per square centimeter second degree Celsius ($cal_{th}\ cm^{-2}\ s^{-1}\ {}^{\circ}C^{-1}$)	4.1840×10^4
1 kilocalorie (I.T.) per square meter hour degree Kelvin ($kcal_{IT}\ m^{-2}\ h^{-1}\ K^{-1}$)	1.163 00
1 watt per square centimeter degree Kelvin ($W\ cm^{-2}\ K^{-1}$)	1.0×10^4
1 watt per square meter degree Kelvin ($W\ m^{-2}\ K^{-1}$)	1.0

Table 2.39b. Heat transfer coefficient (thermal conductance) interconversion factors

from \ to	$W\ m^{-2}\ K^{-1}$	$W\ cm^{-2}\ K^{-1}$	$cal_{IT}\ cm^{-2}\ s^{-1}\ K^{-1}$	$kcal_{IT}\ m^{-2}\ h^{-1}\ K^{-1}$	$Btu\ ft^{-2}\ s^{-1}\ {}^{\circ}F^{-1}$	$Btu\ ft^{-2}\ h^{-1}\ {}^{\circ}F^{-1}$
1 watt per square meter degree Kelvin ($W\ m^{-2}\ K^{-1}$)	1.0	1.0×10^{-4}	$2.388\,46 \times 10^{-5}$	0.859 845	$4.891\,95 \times 10^{-5}$	0.176 11
1 watt per square centimeter degree Kelvin ($W\ cm^{-2}\ K^{-1}$)	1.0×10^{4}	1.0	0.238 846	$8.598\,45 \times 10^{3}$	0.489 195	1.7611×10^{3}
1 calorie (I.T.) per square centimeter second degree Kelvin ($cal_{IT}\ cm^{-2}\ s^{-1}\ K^{-1}$)	4.1868×10^{4}	4.1868	1.0	3.6×10^{4}	2.048 16	$7.373\,38 \times 10^{3}$
1 kilocalorie (I.T.) per square meter hour degree Kelvin ($kcal_{IT}\ m^{-2}\ h^{-1}\ K^{-1}$)	1.163	1.163×10^{-4}	$2.777\,78 \times 10^{-5}$	1.0	$5.689\,34 \times 10^{-5}$	0.204 816
1 British thermal unit per square foot second degree Fahrenheit ($Btu\ ft^{-2}\ s^{-1}\ {}^{\circ}F^{-1}$)	$2.044\,17 \times 10^{4}$	2.044 17	0.488 243	$1.757\,67 \times 10^{4}$	1.0	3.6×10^{3}
1 British thermal unit per square foot hour degree Fahrenheit ($Btu\ ft^{-2}\ h^{-1}\ {}^{\circ}F^{-1}$)	5.678 26	$5.678\,26 \times 10^{-4}$	$1.356\,23 \times 10^{-4}$	4.882 43	$2.777\,78 \times 10^{-4}$	1.0

2.40 Heat release rate (W m^{-3})

The heat release rate is the ratio between the heat and the product of volume and time.

The different units commonly used to express heat release rate are summarized in Table 2.40a. The interconversion factors for the units are presented in Table 2.40b.

Table 2.40a. Miscellaneous units for heat release rate

Unit	W m^{-3}
1 British thermal unit per cubic foot hour (Btu ft^{-3} h^{-1})	10.3497
1 calorie (I.T.) per cubic centimeter second (cal_{IT} cm^{-3} s^{-1})	4.1868×10^6
1 kilocalorie (I.T.) per cubic meter hour ($kcal_{IT}$ m^{-3} h^{-1})	1.163
1 watt per cubic centimeter (W cm^{-3})	1.0×10^6
1 watt per cubic meter (W m^{-3})	1.0

Table 2.40b. Heat release rate interconversion factors

from \ to	$W\ m^{-3}$	$kcal_{IT}\ m^{-3}\ h^{-1}$	$Btu\ ft^{-3}\ h^{-1}$	$W\ cm^{-3}$	$cal_{IT}\ cm^{-3}\ s^{-1}$
1 watt per cubic meter ($W\ m^{-3}$)	1.0	0.859 845	0.096 621 1	1.0×10^{-6}	$2.388\ 46 \times 10^{-7}$
1 kilocalorie (I.T.) per cubic meter hour ($kcal_{IT}\ m^{-3}\ h^{-1}$)	1.163	1.0	0.112 370	1.163×10^{-6}	$2.777\ 78 \times 10^{-7}$
1 British thermal unit per cubic foot hour ($Btu\ ft^{-3}\ h^{-1}$)	10.3497	8.899 15	1.0	$1.034\ 971 \times 10^{-5}$	$2.471\ 99 \times 10^{-6}$
1 watt per cubic centimeter ($W\ cm^{-3}$)	1.0×10^{6}	$8.598\ 45 \times 10^{5}$	9.6621×10^{4}	1.0	0.238 846
1 calorie (I.T.) per cubic centimeter second ($cal_{IT}\ cm^{-3}\ s^{-1}$)	4.1868×10^{6}	3.6×10^{6}	$4.045\ 33 \times 10^{5}$	4.1868	1.0

2.41 Gas constant (*R*) ($N\ m^{-2}\ m^3\ mol^{-1}\ K^{-1}$)

According to Avogadro's hypothesis equal volumes (*V*) of all ideal gases under identical pressure (*P*) and temperature (*T*) conditions contain equal numbers of molecules (*n*), which may be expressed as

$$R = \frac{PV}{nT}$$

where

n = number of moles of gas
R = gas constant

The gas constant (*R*) may be expressed in volumetric and thermal units.

Tables 2.41a and 2.41b summarize some of the values found in the technical literature.

Table 2.41a. Gas constant (*R*) values

Energy	Temperature	Mass unit	*R*
calorie (I.T.) (cal_{IT})	K	mole	1.9872
cubic centimeter-atmosphere (cm^3 atm)	K	mole	82.06
liter-atmosphere (l atm)	K	mole	0.082 06
liter-millimeter mercury (l mm Hg)	K	mole	62.37
joule (absolute) (J)	K	mole	8.3143
joule (international)	K	mole	8.312
liter-bar (l bar)	K	mole	0.08315
liter-(kilogram per square meter) (l ($kg\ m^{-2}$))	K	mole	847.9
liter-(kilogram per square centimeter) (l ($kg\ cm^{-2}$))	K	mole	0.084 79
British thermal unit (Btu)	°R	pound-mole	1.9859
cubic foot-(pound per square inch) (ft^3 ($lb\ in^{-2}$))	°R	pound-mole	10.73
cubic foot-atmosphere	°R	pound-mole	0.7302
cubic foot-(pound per square foot) (ft^3 ($lb\ ft^{-2}$))	°R	pound-mole	1.544×10^3
cubic foot-inch mercury (ft^3 in Hg)	°R	pound-mole	21.85
horsepower-hour (hp h)	°R	pound-mole	7.8×10^{-4}
kilowatt-hour (kW h)	°R	pound-mole	5.83×10^{-4}
cubic foot-cm mercury (ft^3 cm Hg)	°R	pound-mole	55.4
cubic inch-(pound per square inch) (in^3 ($lb\ in^{-2}$))	°R	pound-mole	1.8540×10^4
cubic meter-(newton per square meter) (m^3 ($N\ m^{-2}$))	K	kilogram-mole	8.3143×10^3
cubic meter-(kilogram per square meter) (m^3 ($kg\ m^{-2}$))	K	mole	0.847 887

Table 2.41b. Gas constant (R)

Volume	Temperature	moles	atm	psia	mm Hg	cm Hg	in Hg	in H_2O	ft H_2O
cubic foot (ft^3)	K	g	2.9×10^{-3}	0.0426	2.20	0.220	0.0867	1.18	0.0982
		lb	1.31	19.31	999.0	99.9	39.3	535.0	44.6
	°R	g	1.61×10^{-3}	0.023 66	1.22	0.122	0.0482	0.655	0.0546
		lb	0.730	10.73	555.0	55.5	21.8	297.0	24.8
cubic centimeter (cm^3)	K	g	82.05	1.206×10^3	6.24×10^4	6.24×10^3	2.45×10^3	3.34×10^4	2.78×10^3
		lb	3.72×10^4	5.47×10^5	2.83×10^7	2.83×10^6	1.11×10^6	1.51×10^7	1.26×10^6
	°R	g	45.6	670.0	3.46×10^4	3.46×10^3	1.36×10^3	1.85×10^4	1.55×10^3
		lb	2.07×10^4	3.04×10^5	1.57×10^7	1.57×10^6	6.19×10^5	8.41×10^6	7.01×10^5
liter (l)	K	g	0.082 05	1.206	62.4	6.24	2.45	33.4	2.78
		lb	37.2	547.0	2.83×10^4	2.83×10^3	1.113×10^3	1.514×10^4	1.262×10^3
	°R	g	0.0456	0.670	34.6	3.46	1.36	18.5	1.55
		lb	20.7	304.0	1.57×10^4	1.57×10^3	619.0	8.41×10^3	701.0

2.42 Rate constant of second-order reaction ($m^3\ mol^{-1}\ s^{-1}$)

The rate of the reactions of the second-order depends on two concentration terms

$$A + B \longrightarrow X + Y$$

The rate is given by the expression

$$-\frac{d[A]}{dT} = -\frac{d[B]}{dt} = \frac{dx}{dt} = k\,[A]\,[B]$$

The rate constant (k) depends on the reciprocal concentration and reciprocal time ($conc^{-1}\ time^{-1}$). The unit of the rate constant (k) of the first-order reaction is reciprocal time (s^{-1}).

The interconversion factors for the units to express k are given in Table 2.42.

Table 2.42. Rate constant (equivalent second-order) interconversion factors

A \ B	$cm^3\ mol^{-1}\ s^{-1}$	$dm^3\ mol^{-1}\ s^{-1}$	$m^3\ mol^{-1}\ s^{-1}$	$cm^3\ molecule^{-1}\ s^{-1}$	$(mm\ Hg)^{-1}\ s^{-1}$	$atm^{-1}\ s^{-1}$	$ppm^{-1}\ min^{-1}$	$m^2\ kN^{-1}\ s^{-1}$
1 $cm^3\ mol^{-1}\ s^{-1}$	1.0	1.0×10^{-3}	1.0×10^{-6}	1.66×10^{-24}	$1.604 \times 10^{-5}\ T^{-1}$	$0.012\ 19\ T^{-1}$	2.453×10^{-9}	$1.203 \times 10^{-4}\ T^{-1}$
1 $dm^3\ mol^{-1}\ s^{-1}$	1.0×10^{3}	1.0	1.0×10^{3}	1.66×10^{-21}	$1.604 \times 10^{-2}\ T^{-1}$	$12.19\ T^{-1}$	2.453×10^{-6}	$0.1203\ T^{-1}$
1 $m^3\ mol^{-1}\ s^{-1}$	1.0×10^{6}	1.0×10^{3}	1.0	1.66×10^{-18}	$16.04\ T^{-1}$	$1.219 \times 10^{4}\ T^{-1}$	2.453×10^{-3}	$120.3\ T^{-1}$
1 $cm^3\ molecule^{-1}\ s^{-1}$	6.023×10^{23}	6.023×10^{20}	6.023×10^{17}	1.0	$9.658 \times 10^{18}\ T^{-1}$	$7.34 \times 10^{21}\ T^{-1}$	1.478×10^{15}	$7.244 \times 10^{19}\ T^{-1}$
1 $(mm\ Hg)^{-1}\ s^{-1}$	$6.236 \times 10^{4}\ T$	$62.36\ T$	$0.062\ 36\ T$	$1.035 \times 10^{-19}\ T$	1.0	760.0	0.0456	7.500
1 $atm^{-1}\ s^{-1}$	$82.06\ T$	$0.082\ 06\ T$	$8.206 \times 10^{-5}\ T$	$1.362 \times 10^{-22}\ T$	1.316×10^{-3}	1.0	6.0×10^{-5}	9.869×10^{-3}
1 $ppm^{-1}\ min^{-1}$ (at 298 K, 1 atm total pressure)	4.077×10^{8}	4.077×10^{5}	407.7	6.76×10^{-16}	21.93	1.667×10^{4}	1.0	164.5
1 $m^2\ kN^{-1}\ s^{-1}$	$8.314 \times 10^{3}\ T$	$8.314\ T$	$8.314 \times 10^{-3}\ T$	$1.38 \times 10^{-20}\ T$	0.1333	101.325	6.079×10^{-3}	1.0

2.43 Rate constant of third-order reaction ($m^6\ mol^{-2}\ s^{-1}$)

The reaction of the third-order is represented by the equation

$$A + B + C \longrightarrow X + Y + Z$$

and the rate of the reaction is given by

$$\frac{dx}{dt} = k\,(A_0 - x)\,(B_0 - x)\,(C_0 - x)$$

The rate constant of the third-order reaction (k) depends on the reciprocal of the square of the concentration and the reciprocal time ($conc^{-2}\ time^{-1}$).

The interconversion factors to express k are given in Table 2.43.

Table 2.43. Rate constant (equivalent third-order) interconversion factors

A \ B	$cm^6\ mol^{-2}\ s^{-1}$	$dm^6\ mol^{-2}\ s^{-1}$	$m^6\ mol^{-2}\ s^{-1}$	$cm^6\ molecule^{-2}\ s^{-1}$	$(mm\ Hg)^{-2}\ s^{-1}$	$atm^{-2}\ s^{-1}$	$ppm^{-2}\ min^{-1}$	$m^4\ kN^{-2}\ s^{-1}$
1 $cm^6\ mol^{-2}\ s^{-1}$	1.0	1.0×10^{-6}	1.0×10^{-12}	2.76×10^{-48}	$2.57 \times 10^{-10}\ T^{-2}$	$1.48 \times 10^{-4}\ T^{-2}$	1.003×10^{-19}	$1.447 \times 10^{-8}\ T^{-2}$
1 $dm^6\ mol^{-2}\ s^{-1}$	1.0×10^{6}	1.0	1.0×10^{-6}	2.76×10^{-42}	$2.57 \times 10^{-4}\ T^{-2}$	$148\ T^{-2}$	1.003×10^{-13}	$0.014\,47\ T^{-2}$
1 $m^6\ mol^{-2}\ s^{-1}$	1.0×10^{12}	1.0×10^{6}	1.0	2.76×10^{-36}	$257\ T^{-2}$	$1.48 \times 10^{8}\ T^{-2}$	1.003×10^{-7}	$1.447 \times 10^{4}\ T^{-2}$
1 $cm^6\ molecule^{-2}\ s^{-1}$	3.628×10^{47}	3.628×10^{41}	3.628×10^{35}	1.0	$9.328 \times 10^{37}\ T^{-2}$	$5.388 \times 10^{43}\ T^{-2}$	3.64×10^{28}	$5.248 \times 10^{39}\ T^{-2}$
1 $(mm\ Hg)^{-2}\ s^{-1}$	$3.89 \times 10^{9}\ T^2$	$3.89 \times 10^{3}\ T^2$	$3.89 \times 10^{-3}\ T^2$	$1.07 \times 10^{-38}\ T^2$	1.0	5.776×10^{5}	3.46×10^{-5}	56.25
1 $atm^{-2}\ s^{-1}$	$6.733 \times 10^{3}\ T^2$	$6.733 \times 10^{-3}\ T^2$	$6.733 \times 10^{-9}\ T^2$	$1.86 \times 10^{-44}\ T^2$	1.73×10^{-6}	1.0	6.0×10^{-11}	9.74×10^{-5}
1 $ppm^{-2}\ min^{-1}$ (at 298 K, 1 atm total pressure)	9.97×10^{18}	9.97×10^{12}	9.97×10^{6}	2.75×10^{-29}	2.89×10^{4}	1.667×10^{10}	1.0	1.623×10^{6}
1 $m^4\ kN^{-2}\ s^{-1}$	$6.91 \times 10^{7}\ T^2$	$6.91\ T^2$	$6.91 \times 10^{-4}\ T^2$	$1.904 \times 10^{-40}\ T^2$	0.0178	1.027×10^{4}	6.16×10^{-7}	1.0

2.44 Permeability coefficient ($m^3\ m\ s^{-1}\ m^{-2}\ Pa^{-1}$)

The permeability coefficient characterizes the rate of permeate molecules through a polymer membrane. It may be expressed by:

$$\frac{\text{(amount of permeant) (film thickness)}}{\text{(area) (time) (pressure drop across the film)}}$$

The interconversion factors for the units of permeability coefficient are given in Table 2.44.

Table 2.44. Permeability coefficient interconversion factors

from \ to	$cm^3\ cm\ s^{-1}\ cm^{-2}\ (cm\ Hg)^{-1}$	$cm^3\ cm\ s^{-1}\ cm^{-2}\ (N\ m^{-2})^{-1}$	$cm^3\ cm\ d^{-1}\ m^{-2}\ atm^{-1}$
1 $cm^3\ cm\ s^{-1}\ cm^{-2}\ (cm\ Hg)^{-1}$	1.0	7.5×10^{-4}	6.57×10^{10}
1 $cm^3\ mm\ s^{-1}\ cm^{-2}\ (cm\ Hg)^{-1}$	0.10	7.5×10^{-5}	6.57×10^{9}
1 $cm^3\ cm\ s^{-1}\ cm^{-2}\ atm^{-1}$	0.0132	9.9×10^{-6}	8.64×10^{8}
1 $cm^3\ mil\ d^{-1}\ m^{-2}\ atm^{-1}$	3.87×10^{-14}	2.90×10^{-17}	2.54×10^{-3}
1 $in^3\ mil\ d^{-1}\ (100\ in^2)^{-1}\ atm^{-1}$	9.82×10^{-12}	7.37×10^{-15}	0.646
1 $cm^3\ cm\ d^{-1}\ m^{-2}\ atm^{-1}$	1.52×10^{-11}	1.14×10^{-14}	1.0

2.45 Transmission rate ($kg\ m\ m^{-2}\ s^{-1}$)

If a permeant interacts with polymer molecules, the permeability coefficient is not constant and it depends on the pressure, thickness and other conditions. To obtain a better representation for the permeability of a polymer, the transmission rate is more characteristically

$$\frac{\text{(amount of permeant) (film thickness)}}{\text{(area) (time)}}$$

In this case the saturated vapor pressure of the permeant at a specified temperature is applied across the film.

The interconversion factors for the units of transmission rate are given in Table 2.45.

Table 2.45. Transmission rate interconversion factors

from \ to	$g\ cm\ m^{-2}\ d^{-1}$	$g\ mil\ m^{-2}\ d^{-1}$	$g\ mil\ (100\ m^2)^{-1}\ h^{-1}$	$g\ mil\ (100\ in^2)^{-1}\ h^{-1}$
1 $g\ cm\ m^{-2}\ d^{-1}$	1.0	394.0	1.64×10^{3}	1.06
1 $g\ mil\ m^{-2}\ d^{-1}$	2.54×10^{-3}	1.0	4.17	2.69×10^{-3}
1 $g\ mil\ (100\ m^2)^{-1}\ h^{-1}$	6.10×10^{-4}	0.24	1.0	6.45×10^{-4}
1 $g\ mil\ (100\ m^2)^{-1}\ h^{-1}$	0.945	372.0	1.55×10^{3}	1.0

2.46 Electric charge (quantity of electricity) (C)

The SI unit of electric charge is the coulomb. It is defined as charge transported in 1 second by a current of 1 ampere (A)

$$1\,\text{C} = 1\,\text{A s}$$

Units of electric charge are listed in Table 2.46a. Interconversion factors for various units of electric charge are given in Table 2.46b.

Table 2.46a. Miscellaneous units of electric charge

Unit	C
1 abcoulomb	10.0
1 ampere-hour	3.6×10^{3}
1 ampere-second	1.0
1 coulomb (C)	1.0
1 coulomb (international)	0.999 835
1 electric charge	$1.602\,09 \times 10^{-19}$
1 EM cgs unit of electric charge	10.0
1 ES cgs unit of electric charge	$3.335\,635 \times 10^{-10}$
1 Faraday	
chemical	$9.648\,998 \times 10^{4}$
physical	$9.651\,708 \times 10^{4}$
1 franklin (Fr)	$3.335\,635 \times 10^{-10}$
1 mks unit of electric charge	1.0
1 statcoulomb	$3.335\,635 \times 10^{-10}$

Table 2.46b. Electric charge interconversion factors

from \ to	coulomb	abcoulomb	ampere-hour	coulomb (int.)	electric charge	statcoulomb	faraday (chem.)
1 coulomb (C)	1.0	0.1	2.7778×10^{-4}	1.000 165	$6.241\,96 \times 10^{18}$	$2.997\,93 \times 10^{9}$	$1.036\,377 \times 10^{-5}$
1 abcoulomb	10.0	1.0	0.002 777 8	10.001 65	$6.241\,96 \times 10^{19}$	$2.997\,93 \times 10^{10}$	$1.036\,377 \times 10^{-4}$
1 ampere-hour	3.6×10^{3}	360.0	1.0	$3.600\,594 \times 10^{3}$	$2.247\,106 \times 10^{22}$	$1.079\,255 \times 10^{13}$	0.037 309
1 coulomb (int.)	0.999 835	0.099 983 5	$2.777\,318\,6 \times 10^{-4}$	1.0	$6.240\,931\,3 \times 10^{18}$	$2.997\,436 \times 10^{-9}$	$1.036\,19 \times 10^{-5}$
1 electric charge	$1.602\,09 \times 10^{-19}$	$1.602\,09 \times 10^{-20}$	$4.450\,249 \times 10^{-23}$	$1.602\,354 \times 10^{-19}$	1.0	$4.802\,866\,3 \times 10^{-10}$	$1.660\,339 \times 10^{-24}$
1 statcoulomb	$3.335\,635 \times 10^{-10}$	$3.335\,635 \times 10^{-11}$	$9.265\,650 \times 10^{-14}$	$3.336\,184\,3 \times 10^{-10}$	$2.082\,090 \times 10^{9}$	1.0	$3.456\,975 \times 10^{-15}$
1 faraday (chem.)	$9.648\,998 \times 10^{4}$	$9.648\,998 \times 10^{3}$	26.802 764 7	$9.650\,587\,4 \times 10^{4}$	$6.022\,865 \times 10^{23}$	$2.892\,701 \times 10^{14}$	1.0

2.47 Electric potential difference (voltage) (V)

The electric potential difference between two points in an electric field of strength E is the line integral from E_1 to E_2

$$V = \int_{E_1}^{E_2} E \, dx$$

where x is the distance between the two points. The voltage may also be expressed as the ratio between the energy (in joule) and the electric charge (in coulomb)

$$\text{voltage (V)} = \frac{\text{energy (J)}}{\text{electric charge (C)}}$$

The SI unit of electric potential difference is the volt.

The interconversion factors between the various units of voltage are given in Table 2.47.

Table 2.47. Electric potential difference (voltage) interconversion factors

from \ to	volt	abvolt	statvolt	volt (int.)	microvolt	millivolt
1 volt	1.0	1.0×10^{8}	$3.335\,635 \times 10^{-3}$	0.999 670	1.0×10^{6}	1.0×10^{3}
1 abvolt	1.0×10^{-8}	1.0	$3.335\,635 \times 10^{-11}$	9.9967×10^{-9}	0.01	1.0×10^{-5}
1 statvolt	299.7930	$2.997\,93 \times 10^{10}$	1.0	299.694 07	$2.997\,93 \times 10^{8}$	$2.997\,930 \times 10^{5}$
1 volt (int.)	1.000 330	$1.000\,33 \times 10^{8}$	$3.336\,736 \times 10^{-3}$	1.0	$1.000\,330 \times 10^{6}$	$1.000\,330 \times 10^{3}$
1 microvolt	1.0×10^{-6}	100.0	$3.335\,634\,9 \times 10^{-9}$	$9.996\,70 \times 10^{-7}$	1.0	1.0×10^{-3}
1 millivolt	1.0×10^{-3}	1.0×10^{5}	$3.335\,635 \times 10^{-6}$	$9.996\,70 \times 10^{-4}$	1.0×10^{3}	1.0

2.48 Electric current (amperage) (A)

The SI unit of electric current is the ampere. It is defined as a constant current passing in two straight parallel conductors of infinite length and placed 1 meter apart in vacuum and the current produces a force equal to 2×10^{-7} N m^{-1}.

The interconversion factors between the units of electric current are tabulated (*see* Table 2.48).

Table 2.48. Electric current (amperage) interconversion factors

from \ to	ampere	abampere	ampere (int.)	statampere	faraday (chem.) s^{-1}	faraday (phys.) s^{-1}
1 ampere ($C\ s^{-1}$)	1.0	0.1	1.000 165	$2.997\,93 \times 10^{9}$	$1.036\,377 \times 10^{-5}$	$1.036\,086 \times 10^{-5}$
1 abampere	10.0	1.0	10.001 65	$2.997\,930 \times 10^{10}$	$1.036\,377 \times 10^{-4}$	$1.036\,086 \times 10^{-4}$
1 ampere (int.)	0.999 835	0.099 983 5	1.0	$2.997\,435 \times 10^{9}$	$1.036\,206 \times 10^{-5}$	$1.035\,92 \times 10^{-5}$
1 statampere	$3.335\,635 \times 10^{-10}$	$3.335\,635 \times 10^{-11}$	$3.336\,185\,7 \times 10^{-10}$	1.0	$3.456\,975\,6 \times 10^{-15}$	$3.456\,021\,5 \times 10^{-15}$
1 faraday (chemical) per second	$9.648\,998 \times 10^{4}$	$9.648\,998 \times 10^{3}$	$9.650\,590\,7 \times 10^{4}$	$2.892\,701\,9 \times 10^{14}$	1.0	0.999 724
1 faraday (physical) per second	$9.651\,708 \times 10^{4}$	$9.651\,708 \times 10^{3}$	$9.653\,255 \times 10^{4}$	$2.893\,500\,5 \times 10^{14}$	1.000 276 08	1.0

2.49 Electric current density (linear) (A m^{-1})

The linear electric current density is the current divided by the breadth of the conductor.

The interconversion factors for the units of linear electric current density are given in Table 2.49.

Table 2.49. Electric current density (linear) interconversion factors

from \ to	A m^{-1}	A cm^{-1}	abampere cm^{-1}	ES cgs unit
1 ampere per meter (A m^{-1})	1.0	0.01	1.0×10^{-3}	$2.997\,93 \times 10^{7}$
1 ampere per centimeter (A cm^{-1})	100.0	1.0	0.1	$2.997\,93 \times 10^{9}$
1 abampere per centimeter (abampere cm^{-1})	1.0×10^{3}	10.0	1.0	$2.997\,93 \times 10^{10}$
1 ES cgs unit	$3.335\,635 \times 10^{-8}$	$3.335\,635 \times 10^{-10}$	$3.335\,635 \times 10^{-11}$	1.0

2.50 Electric current density (A m^{-2})

The electric current is the integral of the electric current density with respect to area.

The interconversion factors for the units of electric current density are given in Table 2.50.

Table 2.50. Electric current density interconversion factors

from \ to	$A\ m^{-2}$	$A\ cm^{-2}$	$A\ in^{-2}$	abampere cm^{-2}	$A\ mil^{-2}$
1 ampere per square meter (mks unit) ($A\ m^{-2}$)	1.0	1.0×10^{-4}	6.4516×10^{-4}	1.0×10^{-5}	6.4516×10^{-10}
1 ampere per square centimeter (cgs unit of volume current density) ($A\ cm^{-2}$)	1.0×10^{4}	1.0	6.4516	0.1	6.4516×10^{-6}
1 ampere per square inch ($A\ in^{-2}$)	$1.550\,003\,1 \times 10^{3}$	0.155 000 31	1.0	0.015 500 031	1.0×10^{-6}
1 abampere per square centimeter (EM cgs unit) (abampere cm^{-2})	1.0×10^{5}	10.0	64.516	1.0	6.4516×10^{-5}
1 ampere per square mil ($A\ mil^{-2}$)	$1.550\,003\,1 \times 10^{9}$	$1.550\,003\,1 \times 10^{5}$	1.0×10^{6}	$1.550\,003\,1 \times 10^{4}$	1.0

2.51 Electric resistance (ohm, Ω)

The electric resistance (R) is defined as the ratio between the electric potential difference (V) and the electric current (I) when there is no electromotive force in a conductor.

$$R = \frac{V}{I}$$

The interconversion factors for the units of electric resistance are given in Table 2.51.

Table 2.51. Electric resistance interconversion factors

from \ to	ohm	abohm	megohm	microhm	statohm	ohm (int.)
1 ohm (cgs unit) (Ω)	1.0	1.0×10^{9}	1.0×10^{-6}	1.0×10^{6}	$1.112\,646 \times 10^{-12}$	0.999 505
1 abohm	1.0×10^{-9}	1.0	1.0×10^{-15}	1.0×10^{-3}	$1.112\,646 \times 10^{-21}$	$9.995\,05 \times 10^{-10}$
1 megohm	1.0×10^{6}	1.0×10^{15}	1.0	1.0×10^{12}	$1.112\,646 \times 10^{-6}$	$9.995\,05 \times 10^{5}$
1 microhm	1.0×10^{-6}	1.0×10^{3}	1.0×10^{-12}	1.0	$1.112\,646 \times 10^{-18}$	$9.995\,05 \times 10^{-7}$
1 statohm (ES cgs unit)	$8.987\,584 \times 10^{11}$	$8.987\,584 \times 10^{20}$	$8.987\,584 \times 10^{5}$	$8.987\,584 \times 10^{17}$	1.0	$8.983\,136 \times 10^{11}$
1 ohm (int.)	1.000 495	$1.000\,495 \times 10^{9}$	$1.000\,495 \times 10^{-6}$	$1.000\,495 \times 10^{6}$	$1.113\,197 \times 10^{-12}$	1.0

2.52 Electric conductance (ohm^{-1})

The electric conductance is the reciprocal of the electric resistance (*see* 2.51).

The interconversion factors for the units of electrical conductance are tabulated (*see* Table 2.52).

Table 2.52. Electric conductance interconversion factors

from \ to	mho	abmho	mho (int.)	statmho	megamho
1 mho (siemens, s) (ohm^{-1})	1.0	1.0×10^{-9}	1.000 495	$8.987\,584 \times 10^{11}$	1.0×10^{6}
1 abmho	1.0×10^{9}	1.0	$1.000\,495 \times 10^{9}$	$8.987\,584 \times 10^{20}$	1.0×10^{3}
1 mho (int.)	0.999 505	$9.995\,05 \times 10^{-10}$	1.0	$8.983\,137\,8 \times 10^{11}$	$9.995\,052 \times 10^{-7}$
1 statmho	$1.112\,646 \times 10^{-12}$	$1.112\,646 \times 10^{-21}$	$1.113\,196\,7 \times 10^{-12}$	1.0	$1.112\,646 \times 10^{-18}$
1 megamho	1.0×10^{-6}	1.0×10^{-3}	$1.000\,495 \times 10^{6}$	$8.987\,584 \times 10^{17}$	1.0

2.53 Electrical conductivity ($ohm^{-1}\ m^{-1}$)

The electrical conductivity is the reciprocal of the electrical resistivity (*see* 2.54).

The interconversion factors for the units of electrical conductivity are given in Table 2.53.

Table 2.53. Electrical conductivity (specific conductance) interconversion factors

from \ to	mho m^{-1}	mho cm^{-1}	abmho cm^{-1}	megmho cm^{-1}	megmho in^{-1}	mho-ft (circ. mil)$^{-1}$
1 mho per meter (siemen per meter)	1.0	0.01	1.0×10^{-11}	1.0×10^{-8}	0.025 40	$1.662\,426 \times 10^{-9}$
1 mho per centimeter	100.0	1.0	1.0×10^{-9}	1.0×10^{-6}	2.540	$1.662\,426 \times 10^{-7}$
1 abmho per centimeter	1.0×10^{11}	1.0×10^{9}	1.0	1.0×10^{3}	2.540×10^{9}	$1.662\,426 \times 10^{2}$
1 megmho per centimeter	1.0×10^{8}	1.0×10^{6}	1.0×10^{-3}	1.0	2.540×10^{6}	0.166 242 6
1 megmho per inch	39.370 079	0.393 700 79	$0.393\,700\,79 \times 10^{-9}$	$3.937\,007\,9 \times 10^{-7}$	1.0	$6.544\,985 \times 10^{-8}$
1 mho-foot per circular mill	$6.015\,304\,9 \times 10^{8}$	$6.015\,304\,9 \times 10^{6}$	$6.015\,304\,9 \times 10^{-3}$	6.015 304 9	$1.527\,887 \times 10^{7}$	1.0

2.54 Electric resistivity (specific resistance) (ohm-m)

The electric resistivity is defined as the product of the electric resistance and the cross-sectional area, divided by the length.

Some of the more common units of electric resistivity are listed in Table 2.54a. The interconversion factors for the units are given in Table 2.54b.

Table 2.54a. Miscellaneous units of electric resistivity

1 microhm-centimeter	1.0×10^3 abohm-cm 6.015 349 ohm-circ. mil ft^{-1} 0.393 700 79 microhm-in 1.0×10^{-6} ohm-cm
1 microhm-inch	15.278 875 ohm-circ. mil ft^{-1} 2.54 microhm-cm
1 ohm-meter	10^{11} abohm-cm (EM cgs unit) $1.112\,646 \times 10^{-10}$ (ES cgs unit) 1 mks unit $1.112\,646 \times 10^{-10}$ statohm-cm
1 ohm (mil foot)	1 ohm-circ. mil ft^{-1} $1.662\,426 \times 10^{-7}$ ohm-cm

Table 2.54b. Electric resistivity interconversion factors

from \ to	ohm-m	ohm mm^2 m^{-1}	ohm-mil	ohm-in	ohm (100 ft)$^{-1}$	ohm km^{-1}	(ohm-mil ft^{-1}
1 ohm-meter (ohm-m)	1.0	1.0×10^{6}	100.0	39.370 08	0.032 808	1.0×10^{-3}	6.0153×10^{8}
1 ohm-square millimeter per meter (ohm-mm^2 m^{-1})	1.0×10^{-6}	1.0	1.0×10^{-4}	3.937×10^{-5}	3.2808×10^{-8}	1.0×10^{-9}	601.53
1 ohm-centimeter (ohm-cm)	0.01	1.0×10^{4}	1.0	0.393 700 8	3.2808×10^{-4}	1.0×10^{-5}	6.0153×10^{6}
1 ohm-inch (ohm-in)	0.0254	2.54×10^{4}	2.54	1.0	8.3333×10^{-4}	2.54×10^{-5}	1.5279×10^{7}
1 ohm per 100 feet (ohm (100 ft)$^{-1}$)	30.48	3.048×10^{7}	3.048×10^{3}	1.2×10^{3}	1.0	0.030 48	1.8334×10^{10}
1 ohm per kilometer (ohm km^{-1})	1.0×10^{3}	1.0×10^{9}	1.0×10^{5}	3.937×10^{4}	32.8083	1.0	6.0152×10^{11}
1 ohm-mil per foot (ohm-mil ft^{-1})	1.6624×10^{-9}	1.6624×10^{-3}	1.6624×10^{-7}	6.545×10^{-8}	5.4542×10^{-11}	1.6624×10^{-12}	1.0

2.55 Electric capacitance (F)

The electric capacitance is expressed as the ratio between the electric charge (C) and the electric potential difference (V)

$$\text{electric capacitance (F)} = \frac{C}{V}$$

The interconversion factors for the units of electric capacitance are given in Table 2.55.

Table 2.55. Electric capacitance interconversion factors

from \ to	farad	abfarad	farad (international)	microfarad	statfarad
1 farad (F)	1.0	1.0×10^{-9}	1.000 495	1.0×10^{6}	$8.987\,584 \times 10^{11}$
1 abfarad (EM cgs unit)	1.0×10^{9}	1.0	$1.000\,495 \times 10^{9}$	1.0×10^{15}	$8.987\,584 \times 10^{20}$
1 farad (international before 1948)	0.999 505	$9.995\,052 \times 10^{-10}$	1.0	$9.995\,052 \times 10^{5}$	$8.983\,136\,9 \times 10^{11}$
1 microfarad (μ F)	1.0×10^{-6}	1.0×10^{-15}	$1.000\,495 \times 10^{-6}$	1.0	$8.987\,584 \times 10^{5}$
1 statfarad (ES cgs unit)	$1.112\,646 \times 10^{-12}$	$1.112\,646 \times 10^{-21}$	$1.113\,196\,8 \times 10^{-12}$	$1.112\,646 \times 10^{-6}$	1.0

2.56 Permittivity (F m^{-1})

The ratio between the electric field strength and the displacement is the permittivity. It is sometimes also called capacitivity.

The interconversion factors for the units of permittivity are given in Table 2.56.

Table 2.56. Permittivity interconversion factors

from \ to	F m^{-1}	F cm^{-1}	F in^{-1}	F ft^{-1}	F yd^{-1}
1 farad per meter (F m^{-1})	1.0	0.01	0.025 40	0.304 80	0.914 400 2
1 farad per centimeter (F cm^{-1})	100.0	1.0	2.540	30.480	91.440 02
1 farad per inch (F in^{-1})	39.3701	0.393 701	1.0	12.0	36.0
1 farad per foot (F ft^{-1})	3.280 84	0.032 808 4	0.083 333 3	1.0	3.0
1 farad per yard (F yd^{-1})	1.093 613	0.010 936 13	0.027 777 8	0.333 333	1.0

2.57 Electric field strength (electric field intensity) (V m^{-1})

Electric field strength is defined as the ratio between the force exerted by an electric field and the electric charge.

The interconversion factors for the units of electric field strength are given in Table 2.57.

The following conversion factors may be useful to remember

1 volt cm^{-1} = 3.335 635 × 10^{-3} statvolt cm^{-1}
= 8.472 516 × 10^{-3} statvolt in^{-1}
= 2.540 × 10^{8} abvolt in^{-1}

Table 2.57. Electric field strength interconversion factors

from \ to	$V\ cm^{-1}$	$V\ in^{-1}$	$V\ mil^{-1}$	$kV\ cm^{-1}$	$V_{int}\ cm^{-1}$	$V\ m^{-1}$	$abvolt\ cm^{-1}$
1 volt per centimeter ($V\ cm^{-1}$)	1.0	2.539 998 6	$2.539\ 998\ 6 \times 10^{-3}$	1.0×10^{-3}	0.999 670	100.0	1.0×10^{8}
1 volt per inch ($V\ in^{-1}$)	0.393 701	1.0	1.0×10^{-3}	$3.937\ 01 \times 10^{-4}$	0.393 571	39.3701	$3.937\ 01 \times 10^{7}$
1 volt per mil ($V\ mil^{-1}$)	393.701	1.0×10^{3}	1.0	0.393 701	393.571	$3.937\ 01 \times 10^{4}$	$3.937\ 01 \times 10^{10}$
1 kilovolt per centimeter ($kV\ cm^{-1}$)	1.0×10^{3}	$2.539\ 998\ 6 \times 10^{3}$	2.539 998 6	1.0	999.6698	1.0×10^{5}	1.0×10^{11}
1 volt (int.) per centimeter ($V_{int}\ cm^{-1}$)	1.000 330 3	2.540 837 6	$2.540\ 837\ 5 \times 10^{-3}$	$1.000\ 330\ 3 \times 10^{-3}$	1.0	100.033 03	$1.000\ 330\ 3 \times 10^{8}$
1 volt per meter ($V\ m^{-1}$)	0.01	0.025 399 986	$2.539\ 998\ 6 \times 10^{-5}$	1.0×10^{-5}	$9.996\ 698 \times 10^{-3}$	1.0	1.0×10^{6}
1 abvolt per centimeter ($abvolt\ cm^{-1}$)	1.0×10^{-8}	$2.539\ 998\ 6 \times 10^{-8}$	$2.539\ 998\ 6 \times 10^{-11}$	1.0×10^{-11}	$9.996\ 698 \times 10^{-9}$	1.0×10^{-6}	1.0

2.58 Electric flux density (electric displacement) (C m^{-2})

The electric flux density is the ratio between the electric charge (C) and the surface area. The electric polarization has the same units as electric flux density.

The interconversion factors for the units of electric flux density are given in Table 2.58.

Table 2.58. Electric flux density (electric polarization) interconversion factors

from \ to	C m^{-2}	C cm^{-2}	C in^{-2}	abcoulomb cm^{-2}
1 coulomb per square meter (C m^{-2})	1.0	1.0×10^{-4}	6.4516×10^{-4}	1.0×10^{-5}
1 coulomb per square centimeter (C cm^{-2})	1.0×10^{4}	1.0	6.4516	0.1
1 coulomb per square inch (C in^{-2})	1.550×10^{3}	0.1550	1.0	0.015 50
1 abcoulomb per square centimeter (abcoulomb cm^{-2})	1.0×10^{5}	10.0	64.516×10^{-3}	1.0

2.59 Electric charge density (volume density of charge) (C m^{-3})

The electric charge density is the ratio between the electric charge and volume.

The interconversion factors for the units of electric charge density are given in Table 2.59.

Table 2.59. Electric charge density (volume density of charge) interconversion factors

from \ to	C m^{-3}	C cm^{-3}	EM cgs unit	ES cgs unit
1 coulomb per cubic meter (C m^{-3})	1.0	1.0×10^{-6}	1.0×10^{-7}	$2.997\,93 \times 10^{3}$
1 coulomb per cubic centimeter (C cm^{-3})	1.0×10^{6}	1.0	0.1	$2.997\,93 \times 10^{9}$
1 EM cgs unit	1.0×10^{7}	10.0	1.0	$2.997\,93 \times 10^{10}$
1 ES cgs unit	$3.335\,635 \times 10^{-4}$	$3.335\,635 \times 10^{-10}$	$3.335\,635 \times 10^{-11}$	1.0

2.60 Electric dipole moment (C-m)

The vector product of the electric dipole moment and the electric field strength is equal to the moment of the force.

The interconversion factors for the units of electric dipole moment are given in Table 2.60.

Table 2.60. Electric dipole moment interconversion factors

from \ to	C-m	D	esu-cm ($dyn^{1/2}$ cm^2)
1 coulomb-meter (C-m)	1.0	$2.998\,50 \times 10^{29}$	$2.998\,50 \times 10^{11}$
1 debye (D)	3.335×10^{-30}	1.0	1.0×10^{-18}
1 electrostatic unit-centimeter (franklin-centimeter, Fr-cm) ($dyn^{1/2}$ cm^2)	3.335×10^{-12}	1.0×10^{18}	1.0

2.61 Specific charge (C kg^{-1})

The specific charge is defined as the ratio between the electric charge and the mass.

Some units and conversion factors are presented in Table 2.61a. The interconversion factors for the units of specific charge are given in Table 2.61b.

Table 2.61a. Miscellaneous units of electric charge

Unit	C kg^{-1}
1 abcoulomb per kilogram	10.0
1 abcoulomb per pound	22.046 295 7
1 coulomb per kilogram	1.0
1 statcoulomb per kilogram	$3.334\,857 \times 10^{-10}$
1 statcoulomb per pound	$7.352\,254 \times 10^{-10}$

Table 2.61b. Specific charge interconversion factors

from \ to	C kg^{-1}	statcoulomb dyn^{-1}	faraday (chem.) kg^{-1}	faraday (phys.) kg^{-1}
1 coulomb per kilogram (C kg^{-1})	1.0	3.0577×10^{3}	$1.036\,38 \times 10^{-5}$	$1.036\,09 \times 10^{-5}$
1 statcoulomb per dyne (statcoulomb dyn^{-1})	$3.270\,43 \times 10^{-4}$	1.0	$3.389\,410 \times 10^{-9}$	$3.388\,46 \times 10^{-9}$
1 faraday (chemical) per kilogram	$9.648\,97 \times 10^{4}$	$2.950\,365\,6 \times 10^{8}$	1.0	0.999 720
1 faraday (physical) per kilogram	$9.651\,671 \times 10^{4}$	$2.951\,191\,4 \times 10^{8}$	1.000 279 90	1.0

2.62 Inductance (permeance) (H)

The inductance is defined as the ratio between the magnetic flux through a loop caused by a current in the loop and the electric current.

The interconversion factors for the units of inductance are given in Table 2.62.

Table 2.62. Inductance (permeance) interconversion factors

from \ to	H	abhenry	millihenry mH	stathenry	ES cgs unit	H_{int}
1 henry (H)	1.0	1.0×10^{9}	1.0×10^{3}	$1.112\,646 \times 10^{-12}$	$1.112\,646 \times 10^{-12}$	0.999 505
1 abhenry (EM cgs unit)	1.0×10^{-9}	1.0	1.0×10^{-6}	$1.112\,646 \times 10^{-21}$	$1.112\,646 \times 10^{-21}$	$9.995\,05 \times 10^{-10}$
1 millihenry (mH)	1.0×10^{-3}	1.0×10^{6}	1.0	$1.112\,646 \times 10^{-15}$	$1.112\,646 \times 10^{-15}$	$9.995\,05 \times 10^{-4}$
1 stathenry	$8.987\,584 \times 10^{11}$	$8.987\,584 \times 10^{20}$	$8.987\,584 \times 10^{14}$	1.0	1.0	$8.983\,135\,1 \times 10^{11}$
1 ES cgs unit	$8.987\,584 \times 10^{11}$	$8.987\,584 \times 10^{20}$	$8.987\,584 \times 10^{14}$	1.0	1.0	$8.983\,135\,1 \times 10^{11}$
1 henry (int. before 1948)	1.000 495	$1.000\,495 \times 10^{9}$	$1.000\,495 \times 10^{3}$	$1.113\,197\,1 \times 10^{-12}$	$1.113\,197\,1 \times 10^{-12}$	1.0

2.63 Magnetic permeability (H m^{-1})

The magnetic permeability is expressed as the ratio between the magnetic flux density and the magnetic field strength.

The interconversion factors for the units of magnetic permeability are given in Table 2.63.

Table 2.63a. Magnetic permeability interconversion factors

from \ to	H m^{-1}	maxwell/gilbert	gausse/oersted	ES cgs unit	mks (nr) unit
1 henry per meter (mks (r) unit) (H m^{-1})	1.0	$7.957\,747\,2 \times 10^{7}$	$7.957\,747\,2 \times 10^{5}$	$8.854\,156 \times 10^{-16}$	0.079 577 472
1 maxwell/gilbert	$1.256\,637 \times 10^{-8}$	1.0	0.01	$1.112\,646 \times 10^{-23}$	1.0×10^{-9}
1 gausse/oersted (EM cgs unit)	$1.256\,637 \times 10^{-6}$	100.0	1.0	$1.112\,646 \times 10^{-21}$	1.0×10^{-7}
1 ES cgs unit	$1.129\,413\,1 \times 10^{15}$	$8.987\,583\,9 \times 10^{22}$	$8.987\,583\,9 \times 10^{20}$	1.0	$8.987\,583\,9 \times 10^{13}$
1 mks (nr) unit	12.566 37	1.0×10^{9}	1.0×10^{7}	$1.112\,646 \times 10^{-14}$	1.0

2.64 Magnetic flux (V-s)

The magnetic flux is the scalar product of the magnetic flux density and the area.

The interconversion factors for the units of magnetic flux are given in Table 2.64.

Table 2.64. Magnetic flux interconversion factors

from \ to	weber	maxwell	maxwell (Int.)	statweber	kiloline
1 weber (Volt-second)	1.0	1.0×10^{8}	9.9967×10^{7}	3.3356×10^{-3}	1.0×10^{5}
1 maxwell (line or gauss-cm²)	1.0×10^{-8}	1.0	0.999 67	3.3356×10^{-11}	1.0×10^{-3}
1 maxwell (Int.)	$1.000\ 33 \times 10^{-8}$	1.000 33	1.0	3.3367×10^{-11}	$1.000\ 33 \times 10^{-3}$
1 statweber	299.796	$2.997\ 96 \times 10^{10}$	$2.996\ 972 \times 10^{10}$	1.0	2.99796×10^{7}
1 kiloline	1.0×10^{-5}	1.0×10^{3}	999.67	3.3356×10^{-8}	1.0

2.65 Magnetic flux density (magnetic induction) (V-s m^2)

In the equation, the vector product of the magnetic flux density and the electric current is equal to the force divided by unit length.

The interconversion factors for the units of magnetic flux density are given in Table 2.65.

Table 2.65. Magnetic flux density (magnetic induction) interconversion factors

from \ to	maxwell cm^{-2}	ES cgs unit	maxwell in^{-2}	maxwell (int.) cm^{-2}	maxwell m^{-2}	weber cm^{-2}
1 maxwell cm^{-2} (gauss)	1.0	$3.335\,635 \times 10^{-11}$	6.4516	0.999 670	1.0×10^{4}	1.0×10^{-8}
1 ES cgs unit	$2.997\,93 \times 10^{10}$	1.0	$1.934\,144 \times 10^{11}$	$2.996\,940\,6 \times 10^{10}$	$2.997\,93 \times 10^{14}$	299.7923
1 maxwell in^{-2}	0.155 000 3	$5.170\,244\,2 \times 10^{-12}$	1.0	0.154 949 16	$1.550\,003 \times 10^{3}$	$1.550\,0 \times 10^{-9}$
1 maxwell (int.) cm^{-2}	1.000 33	$3.336\,736 \times 10^{-11}$	6.453 729 8	1.0	$1.000\,33 \times 10^{4}$	$1.000\,328 \times 10^{-8}$
1 maxwell m^{-2}	1.0×10^{-4}	$3.335\,635\,2 \times 10^{-15}$	6.4516×10^{-4}	$9.996\,701 \times 10^{-5}$	1.0	1.0×10^{-12}
1 weber cm^{-2}	1.0×10^{8}	$3.335\,635\,2 \times 10^{-3}$	6.4516×10^{8}	$9.996\,701 \times 10^{7}$	1.0×10^{12}	1.0

1 gauss = 1 maxwell cm^{-2} = 1 line cm^{-2} = 1 abtesla = 1 EM cgs unit of magnetic flux density
1 tesla = 1 weber m^{-2}

2.66 Magnetomotive force (Gb)

The magnetomotive force is defined as the circular integral of the magnetic field strength.

The interconversion factors for the units of magnetomotive force are given in Table 2.66.

Table 2.66. Magnetomotive force interconversion factors

from \ to	gilbert	ampere-turn	abampere-turn	ES cgs unit	gilbert (int.)
1 gilbert	1.0	0.795 774 72	0.079 577 472	$2.997\,93 \times 10^{10}$	1.000 165
1 ampere-turn	1.256 637 05	1.0	0.1	$3.767\,309\,9 \times 10^{10}$	1.256 844 4
1 abampere-turn	12.566 370 5	10.0	1.0	$3.767\,309\,9 \times 10^{11}$	12.568 444
1 ES cgs unit	$3.335\,634\,9 \times 10^{-11}$	$2.654\,413\,9 \times 10^{-11}$	$2.654\,413\,9 \times 10^{-12}$	1.0	$3.336\,185\,3 \times 10^{-11}$
1 gilbert (int.)	0.999 835	0.795 643 44	0.079 564 344	$2.997\,435\,4 \times 10^{10}$	1.0

2.67 Magnetic field strength (intensity of magnetization) (Gb m^{-1})

The magnetic field strength is described by Maxwell's equation, which expresses the sum of the electric current density and the rate of change of displacement with respect to time.

The interconversion factors for the units of magnetic field strength are given in Table 2.67.

Table 2.67. Magnetic field strength (intensity of magnetization) interconversion factors

from \ to	oersted	ampere-turn in^{-1}	ampere-turn m^{-1}	ES cgs unit	oersted (int.)	ampere-turn cm^{-1}
1 oersted (gilbert/cm)	1.0	2.021 267 8	79.577 472	$2.997\,930 \times 10^{10}$	1.000 165	0.795 774 72
1 ampere-turn per inch	0.494 739	1.0	39.370 078 5	$1.483\,192\,8 \times 10^{10}$	0.494 820 6	0.393 700 8
1 ampere-turn per meter	0.012 566 37	0.025 40	1.0	$3.767\,309\,7 \times 10^{8}$	0.012 568 44	0.01
1 ES cgs unit	$3.335\,635 \times 10^{-11}$	$6.742\,211\,8 \times 10^{-11}$	$2.654\,414\,1 \times 10^{-9}$	1.0	$3.336\,184\,4 \times 10^{-11}$	$2.654\,414\,1 \times 10^{-11}$
1 oersted (int.)	0.999 835	2.020 934 9	79.564 366 5	$2.997\,436\,1 \times 10^{10}$	1.0	0.795 643 665
1 ampere-turn per centimeter	1.256 637 05	2.540	100.0	$3.767\,309\,6 \times 10^{10}$	1.256 844 04	1.0

2.68 Reluctance (Gb V^{-1} s^{-1})

The reluctance is defined as the ratio between the magnetic potential difference and the magnetic flux.

The interconversion factors for the units of reluctance are given in Table 2.68.

Table 2.68. Reluctance interconversion factors

from \ to	ampere-turn $weber^{-1}$	gilbert $maxwell^{-1}$	ES cgs unit
1 ampere-turn per weber	1.0	$1.256\,637 \times 10^{-8}$	$1.129\,413 \times 10^{13}$
1 gilbert per maxwell (EM cgs unit)	$7.957\,747 \times 10^{7}$	1.0	$8.987\,583\,5 \times 10^{20}$
1 ES cgs unit	$8.854\,156\,9 \times 10^{-14}$	$1.112\,646 \times 10^{-21}$	1.0

2.69 Luminance (brightness, illumination, illuminance) (cd m^{-2})

The luminance or brightness is characteristic for the light emitted from a surface in the direction of view.

The common units for luminance are summarized in Table 2.69. The interconversion factors for the units are given in Tables 2.69b and 2.69c.

Table 2.69a. Miscellaneous units of luminance

Unit	cd m^{-2}
1 apostilb	3.183 099
1 candle per square centimeter (cd cm^{-2})	1.0×10^{4}
1 candle per square foot (cd ft^{-2})	10.763 910
1 candle per square inch (cd in^{-2})	$1.550\,003 \times 10^{3}$
1 candle per square meter (cd m^{-2})	1.0
1 foot-candle (ft-cd)	3.4263
1 foot-lambert (ft-lambert)	3.4263
1 lambert	$3.183\,098\,9 \times 10^{3}$
1 lumen per square centimeter (lm cm^{-2})	$3.183\,098\,9 \times 10^{3}$
1 lumen per square foot (lm ft^{-2})	3.4263
1 lumen per square meter (lm m^{-2})	0.318 313 7
1 lux (lx)	0.318 313 7
1 meter-candle (m-cd)	0.318 313 7
1 meter-lambert (m-lambert)	3.183 099
1 milliphot	3.183 137
1 nit	1.0
1 nox	$3.183\,137 \times 10^{-4}$
1 phot	$3.183\,098\,9 \times 10^{3}$
1 stilb	1.0×10^{4}

Table 2.69b. Luminance (brightness, illumination, illuminance) interconversion factors

from \ to	cd cm^{-2}	cd ft^{-2}	ft-lambert	lambert	m-lambert	cd in^{-2}	cd m^{-2}
1 candle per square centimeter (stilb) (cd cm^{-2})	1.0	929.03	$2.918\,635\,1 \times 10^3$	3.141 593	$3.141\,59 \times 10^3$	6.4516	1.0×10^4
1 candle per square foot (cd ft^{-2})	$1.076\,391 \times 10^{-3}$	1.0	3.141 592 7	0.003 381 58	3.381 58	0.006 944 4	10.763 91
1 foot-lambert (foot-candle) (ft-lambert)	$3.426\,26 \times 10^{-4}$	0.318 309 9	1.0	$1.076\,391 \times 10^{-3}$	1.076 391	$2.210\,48 \times 10^{-3}$	3.426 26
1 lambert (photo)	0.318 310	295.719 54	929.0304	1.0	1.0×10^3	2.053 60	$3.183\,098\,9 \times 10^3$
1 meter-lambert (apostilb) (m-lambert)	3.1831×10^{-4}	0.295 72	0.929 03	1.0×10^{-3}	1.0	$2.053\,60 \times 10^{-3}$	3.183 099
1 candle per square inch (cd in^{-2})	0.155 000 31	144.0	452.389 34	0.486 947 8	486.9478	1.0	$1.550\,003 \times 10^3$
1 candle per square meter (cd m^{-2})	1.0×10^{-4}	0.092 903	0.291 863 52	$3.141\,592\,6 \times 10^{-4}$	0.314 159 26	$6.451\,60 \times 10^{-4}$	1.0

Table 2.69c. Luminance (brightness, illumination, illuminance) interconversion factors

from \ to	lux	ft-cd	phot	milliphot	nox
1 lux (lumen per square meter)	1.0	0.092 903	1.0×10^{-4}	0.1	1.0×10^{3}
1 foot-candle (lumen per square foot) (ft-cd)	10.763 91	1.0	0.001 076 4	1.076 391	$1.076\ 39 \times 10^{4}$
1 phot (lm cm^{-2})	1.0×10^{4}	929.0304	1.0	1.0×10^{3}	1.0×10^{7}
1 milliphot	10.0	0.929 030 4	1.0×10^{-3}	1.0	1.0×10^{4}
1 nox	1.0×10^{-3}	9.2903×10^{-5}	1.0×10^{-7}	1.0×10^{-4}	1.0

2.70 Luminous flux (lm)

The luminous flux is described as the total visible energy emitted by a source per unit time. In other words, it is the rate of flow of luminous energy.

The interconversion factors for the units of luminous flow are given in Table 2.70.

Table 2.70. Luminous flux interconversion factors

from \ to	lm	candlepower (spherical)	W
1 lumen (candle steradian) (lm)	1.0	0.079 577 47	$1.470\ 59 \times 10^{-3}$
1 candlepower (spherical)	12.566 37	1.0	0.018 479 98
1 watt (maximum visible radiation) (W)	680.0	54.112 680	1.0

2.71 Luminous intensity (cd)

The luminous intensity is the ratio between the luminous flux emitted by a point source and the solid angle of the core.

The interconversion factors for the units of luminous intensity are given in Table 2.71.

Table 2.71. Luminous intensity interconversion factors

from \ to	candle (int.)	carcel unit	Hefner unit	candle (UK)	candle (German)
1 candle (int.) (or candela) (cd(int.))	1.0	0.104	1.11	0.96	0.95
1 carcel unit	9.615	1.0	10.67	9.231	9.135
1 Hefner unit	0.9009	0.093 69	1.0	0.8621	0.8547
1 candle (UK)	1.0417	0.1083	1.16	1.0	0.990
1 candle (German)	1.0526	0.1094	1.17	1.01	1.0

1 candle (int.) = 1 lumen (int.) per stearadian (or stearidan) = 1 candle (pentane) = 1 bougie decimabe

2.72 Optical absorption coefficient (or factor) (m^2 mol^{-1})

The optical absorption coefficient is defined as the ratio of the intensity loss by absorption to the total original intensity of light.

The interconversion factors for the units of optical absorption coefficient are given in Table 2.72.

Table 2.72. Optical absorption coefficient interconversion factors

from \ to	(cross section σ) cm^2 $molecule^{-1}$ base *e*	(atm at 273 K)$^{-1}$ cm^{-1} base *e*	dm^3 mol^{-1} cm^{-1} base 10	cm^2 mol^{-1} base 10
1 (atm at 298 K)$^{-1}$ cm^{-1} base *e*	4.06×10^{-20}	1.09	10.6	1.06×10^4
1 (atm at 298 K)$^{-1}$ cm^{-1} base 10	9.35×10^{-20}	2.51	24.4	2.44×10^4
1 (mm Hg at 298 K)$^{-1}$ cm^{-1} base 10	7.11×10^{-17}	1.91×10^3	1.86×10^4	1.86×10^7
1 (atm at 273 K)$^{-1}$ cm^{-1} base *e*	3.72×10^{-20}	1.0	9.73	9.73×10^3
1 (atm at 273 K)$^{-1}$ cm^{-1} base 10	8.57×10^{-20}	2.303	22.4	2.24×10^4
1 dm^3 mol^{-1} cm^{-1} base 10	3.82×10^{-21}	0.103	1.0	1.0×10^3
1 cm^2 mol^{-1} base 10	3.82×10^{-24}	1.03×10^{-4}	1.0×10^{-3}	1.0
1 cm^2 $molecule^{-1}$ base *e* (cross section σ)	1.0	2.69×10^{19}	2.62×10^{20}	2.62×10^{23}

2.73 Noise level (intensity of noise level) (dB)

The noise level is measured by the sound pressure level of a reference sound compared by an observer to be equally noisy. The reference sound is produced by a band of random noise of width one-third to one octave centred on a frequency of 1000 hertz.

The unit of noise level is often expressed in decibels (dB); 1 decibel is the sound pressure level when

$$20 \log_{10}\left(\frac{p}{p_0}\right) = 1$$

where p and p_0 are a given sound pressure and a reference pressure, respectively. Decibel is often expressed by an alternative word:

decilit
decilog
decilu
decomlog
logit
transition unit

The interconversion factors for the units of noise level are given in Table 2.73.

Table 2.73. Noise level interconversion factors

from \ to	dB	B	Np
1 decibel (dB)	1.0	0.1	0.1151
1 bel (B)	10.0	1.0	1.1510
1 neper (Np)	8.6881	0.868 81	1.0

2.74 Radioactivity (Ci)

The radioactivity is caused by the partial disintegration of the atomic nucleus, followed by the emission of electromagnetic radiation. The rays emitted consist of alpha, beta and gamma particles.

The interconversion factors for the units of radioactivity are given in Table 2.74.

Table 2.74. Radioactivity interconversion factors

from \ to	Ci	Bq	mCi	μ Ci
1 curie (Ci)	1.0	3.70×10^{10}	1.0×10^{3}	1.0×10^{6}
1 becquerel (disintegration per second) (Bq)	$2.702\,703 \times 10^{-11}$	1.0	$2.702\,703 \times 10^{-8}$	$2.702\,703 \times 10^{-5}$
1 millicurie (mCi)	1.0×10^{-3}	3.70×10^{7}	1.0	1.0×10^{3}
1 microcurie (μCi)	1.0×10^{-6}	3.70×10^{4}	1.0×10^{-3}	1.0

2.75 Radiation (exposure to X- or gamma-radiation) (C kg^{-1})

The radiation is defined as the emission and propagation of electromagnetic energy in form of alpha, beta and gamma particles through space or through a material medium in the form of waves.

The interconversion factors for the units of radiation are given in Table 2.75.

Table 2.75. Radiation (exposure to X- or gamma-radiation) interconversion factors

from \ to	R	C kg^{-1}	statcoulomb dyn^{-1}
1 röntgen (R)	1.0	2.58×10^{-4}	0.7889
1 coulomb per kilogram (C kg^{-1})	3.876×10^{3}	1.0	3.0577×10^{3}
1 statcoulomb per dyne (statcoulomb dyn^{-1})	1.267 619	$3.270\,43 \times 10^{-4}$	1.0

2.76 Radiation dose absorbed (ionizing radiation) (J kg^{-1})

The absorbed ionizing radiation dose is defined as the ratio between the absorbed energy and the unit mass.

The interconversion factors for units of ionizing radiation are given in Table 2.76. Further conversion factors of the units are presented in 2.34.

Table 2.76. Radiation dose absorbed (ionizing radiation) interconversion factors

from \ to	rad	J kg^{-1}	Btu lb^{-1}	kcal kg^{-1}
1 rad	1.0	0.01	$4.299\,226 \times 10^{-6}$	$2.388\,46 \times 10^{-6}$
1 joule per kilogram (gray, Gy) (J kg^{-1})	100.0	1.0	$4.299\,23 \times 10^{-4}$	$2.388\,46 \times 10^{-4}$
1 British thermal unit per pound (Btu lb^{-1})	2.326×10^{5}	2.326×10^{3}	1.0	0.555 555 6
1 kilocalorie per kilogram (kcal kg^{-1})	4.1868×10^{5}	4.1868×10^{3}	1.80	1.0

2.77 Radiation dose equivalent (absorbed ionizing radiation dose) (Rem)

The radiation dose equivalent by living tissue produces a biological effect equivalent to the action of one röntgen of electromagnetic radiation. The magnitude of the radiation dose is affected by certain modifying factors, extending from 1 to 20.

The various units of radiation dose equivalent are given in Table 2.77.

Table 2.77. Radiation does equivalent (biologically effective dose) interconversion factors

from \ to	Rem	mRem	μRem
1 röntegen equivalent man (Rem)	1.0	1.0×10^{3}	1.0×10^{6}
1 millirem (mRem)	1.0×10^{-3}	1.0	1.0×10^{3}
1 microrem (μRem)	1.0×10^{-6}	1.0×10^{-3}	1.0

Appendix

Example 1

Show that 1 Btu lb^{-1} $°F^{-1}$ = 1 cal g^{-1} $°C^{-1}$ (*see* 2.36).

1 Btu = 251.996 cal (*see* Table 2.32b)

1 lb = 453.5924 g (*see* Table 2.9b)

1 °F = 5/9 °C (*see* Table 2.31b)

The conversion becomes

$$1 \text{ Btu lb}^{-1}\,°\text{F}^{-1} = \frac{251.996 \text{ cal}}{453.5924 \text{ g} \times 5/9\,°\text{C}} = 1 \text{ cal g}^{-1}\,°\text{C}^{-1}$$

Example 2

Show that 1 cal_{IT} l^{-1} $°C^{-1}$ = 0.004 186 68 J cm^{-3} $°C^{-1}$ (*see* Table 2.36e).

1 cal_{IT} = 4.1868 J (*see* Table 2.32b)

1 l = 1000.028 cm^3 (*see* Table 2.3b)

1 °C = 1 °C (*see* Table 2.31b)

The conversion becomes

$$1 \text{ cal}_{IT}\ \text{l}^{-1}\,°\text{C}^{-1} = \frac{4.1868 \text{ J}}{1000.028 \text{ cm}^3 \times 1\,°\text{C}}$$
$$= 0.004\,186\,68 \text{ J cm}^{-3}\,°\text{C}^{-1}$$

Example 3

Show that 1 lbf s ft^{-2} = 478.803 poise (*see* Table 2.28b).

1 lbf = 444 822 dyn (*see* Table 2.26b)

1 ft^2 = 929.03 cm^{-2} (*see* Table 2.2b)

The conversion becomes

$$1 \text{ lbf s ft}^{-2} = \frac{444\,822 \text{ dyn} \times 1 \text{ s}}{929.03 \text{ cm}^2} = 478.803 \text{ poise}$$

Example 4

Show that 1 Btu in ft^{-2} h^{-1} $°F^{-1}$ = 0.144 228 W m^{-1} $°C^{-1}$ (*see* Table 2.38b).

1 Btu = 1055.06 J (*see* Table 2.32b)

1 in = 0.0254 m (*see* Table 2.1b)

1 ft^2 = 0.092 903 m^2 (*see* Table 2.2b)

1 h = 3600 s (*see* Table 2.5b)

1 °F = 5/9 °C (*see* Table 2.31b)

1 W = 1 J s^{-1} (*see* Table 2.33a)

The conversion becomes

1 Btu in ft^{-2} h^{-1} $°F^{-1}$ =

$$\frac{1055.06 \text{ J}}{(0.092903 \text{ m}^2/0.0254 \text{ m}) \times 3600 \text{ s} \times 5/9\,°\text{C}}$$
$$= 0.144\,228 \text{ W m}^{-1}\,°\text{C}^{-1}$$

Example 5

Show that the gas constant (R) is 8.3143 J mol^{-1} K^{-1} (*see* Tables 2.41a and 2.41e).

An ideal gas consisting of 6.022 045 × 10^{23} molecules (Avogadro number, *see* Table 1.4) at 1 atm total pressure and a temperature of 273.15 K, occupies a standard molar volume (V) of 22 413.83 cm^3. That is

$$P\,V = 22\,413.83 \text{ cm}^3\text{-atm mol}^{-1}$$

According to the ideal gas law

$$P\,V = n\,R\,T = 22\,413.83 \text{ cm}^3\text{-atm mol}^{-1}.$$

For one mole (n = 1) of ideal gas at 273.15 K (T) and 1 atm pressure (P) we obtain the universal gas constant (R) in volumetric unit

$$R = \frac{22\,413.83}{n\,T} = \frac{22\,413.83}{273.15}$$
$$= 82.056\,855 \text{ cm}^3 \text{ atm mol}^{-1}\text{ K}^{-1}$$

From Table 2.32a

$$1 \text{ cm}^3\text{-atm} = 0.101\,325 \text{ J}$$

and the gas constant (R) in calorific unit becomes

$$R = 82.056\,855 \text{ cm}^3 \text{ atm mol}^{-1}\text{ K}^{-1} \times 0.101\,325 \text{ J}$$
$$= 8.314\,41 \text{ J mol}^{-1}\text{ K}^{-1}$$

References

American Chemical Society (1967) *Handbook for Authors of Papers in the Journals of the American Chemical Society*, 127 pp. (Washington, American Chemical Society).

American Petroleum Institute (1970) *Technical Data Book—Petroleum Refining*, 2nd edn. 14 chap. (Washington, DC, American Petroleum Institute).

Anderton, P. and Bigg, P. H. (1969) *Changing to the Metric System*, 3rd edn, 48 pp. (London, HMSO.)

Angus, S., Armstrong, B. and de Reuck, K. M. (1985) *International Thermodynamic Tables of the Fluid State: 8. Chlorine*, 162 pp. (Oxford, Pergamon Press).

Angus, S., de Reuck, K. M. and Armstrong, B. (1979) *International Thermodynamic Tables of the Fluid State: 6. Nitrogen*, 244 pp. (Oxford, Pergamon Press).

Anonymous (1966) *The Radiochemical Manual*, 2nd edn, 327 pp. (Amersham, The Radiochemical Centre).

ASHRAE (1976) *Thermophysical Properties of Refrigerants*, 2nd edn, 237 pp. (New York, American Society of Heating, Refrigeration and Air-Conditioning Engineers).

ASTM Viscosity Index (1965) *ASTM Viscosity Index Calculated from Kinematic Viscosity*, ASTM Data Series DS 39a, 951 pp. (Philadelphia, American Society for Testing and Materials).

Barton, A. F. M. (1975) Solubility parameters. *Chem. Rev.*, **75**(6), 731–53.

Barton, A. F. M. (1983) *CRC Handbook of Solubility Parameters and Other Cohesion Parameters*, 608 pp. (Boca Raton, CRC Press).

Baulch, D. L., Cox, R. A., Hampson, R. F., Kerr, J. A., Troe, J. and Watson, R. T. (1980). Evaluated kinetic and photochemical data for atmospheric chemistry. *J. Phys. Chem. Ref. Data*, **9**(2), 295–471.

Baumeister, T. (ed.) (1967) *Standard Handbook for Mechanical Engineers*, 7th edn, 18 chap. (New York, McGraw-Hill).

Biggs, A. J. (1969) *Direct Reading Two-Way Metric Conversion Tables*, 100 pp. (London, Pitman).

Blackman, D. R. (1969) *SI Units in Engineering*, 56 pp. (Melbourne, Macmillan).

Bolz, R. E. and Tuve, G. L. (ed.) (1970) *Handbook of Tables for Applied Engineering Science*, 975 pp. (Cleveland, The Chemical Rubber Co.).

Brandrup, J. and Immergut, E. H. (ed.) (1975) *Polymer Handbook*, 2nd edn, 8 chap. (New York, John Wiley).

British Standards (1962) *Conversion Factors and Tables. Part 2. Detailed Conversion Tables*, BS350. 293 pp. (London, British Standards Institution).

British Standards (1967) *Additional Tables for SI Conversions*, PD 6203 (suppl. no. 1 to BS350, Part 1), 87 pp. (London, British Standards Institution).

British Standards (1974) *Conversion Factors and Tables. Part 1. Basis of Tables. Conversion Factors*, BS350, 100 pp. (London, British Standards Institution).

British Standards (1981) *Specification for SI Units and Recommendations for the Use of their Multiples and of Certain Other Units*, BS5555 ISO 1000-1981, 17 pp. (London, British Standards Institution).

British Standards (1982) *Specification for Quantities, Units and Symbols. Part 0. General Principles*, BS5775, Pt 0, ISO 31/0-1981, 14 pp. (London, British Standards Institution).

British Standards (1979) *Specification for Quantities, Units and Symbols. Part 1. Space and Time*, BS5775, Pt 1, ISO 31/1-1978, 15 pp. (London, British Standards Institution).

British Standards (1979) *Specification for Quantities, Units and Symbols. Part 2. Periodic and Related Phenomena*, BS5775, Pt 2, ISO-31/2-1978, 8 pp. (London, British Standards Institution).

British Standards (1979) *Specification for Quantities, Units and Symbols. Part 3. Mechanics*, BS5775, Pt 3, ISO 31/3-1978, 20 pp. (London, British Standards Institution).

British Standards (1979) *Specification for Quantities, Units and Symbols. Part 4. Heat*, BS5775, Pt 4, ISO 31/4-1978, 17 pp. (London, British Standards Institution).

British Standards (1980) *Specification for Quantities, Units and Symbols. Part 5. Electricity and Magnetism*, BS5775, Pt 5, ISO 31/5-1979, 26 pp. (London, British Standards Institution).

British Standards (1982) *Specification for Quantities, Units and Symbols. Part 6. Light and Related Electromagnetic Radiations*, BS5775, Pt 6, ISO 31/6-1980, 14 pp. (London, British Standards Institution).

British Standards (1979) *Specification for Quantities, Units and Symbols. Part 7. Acoustics*, BS5775, Pt 7, ISO 31/7-1978, 15 pp. (London, British Standards Institution).

British Standards (1982) *Specification for Quantities, Units and Symbols. Part 8. Physical Chemistry and Molecular Physics*, BS5775, Pt 8, ISO 31/8-1980, 21 pp. (London, British Standards Institution).

British Standards (1982) *Specification for Quantities, Units and Symbols. Part 9. Atomic and Nuclear Physics*, BS5775, Pt 9, ISO 31/9-1980, 15 pp. (London, British Standards Institution).

British Standards (1982) *Specification for Quantities, Units and Symbols. Part 10. Nuclear Reactions and Ionizing Radiations*, BS5775, Pt 10, ISO 31/10, 20 pp. (London, British Standards Institution).

British Standards (1979) *Specification for Quantities, Units and Symbols. Part 11. Mathematical Signs and Symbols for Use in the Physical Sciences and Technology*, BS5775, Pt 11, ISO 31/11-1978, 31 pp. (London, British Standards Institution).

British Standards (1982) *Specification for Quantities, Units and Symbols. Part 12. Dimensionless Parameters*, BS5775, Pt 12, ISO 31/12-1981, 7 pp. (London, British Standards Institution).

British Standards (1982) *Specification for Quantities, Units and Symbols. Part 13. Solid State Physics*, BS5775, Pt 13, ISO 31/13-1981, 19 pp. (London, British Standards Institution).

Busev, A. I. and Efimov, I. P. (1984) *Chemistry. Definitions, Notations Terminology*, 296 pp. (Moscow, Mir).

Canham, W. G. (1972) The international metric system, *Chem. Engng Prog.*, **68**(7), 90–94.

Childs, W. H. J. (1958) *Physical Constants*, 8th edn, 87 pp. (London Methuen); *CA*, **53**, 846d.

Chisholm, L. J. (1967) *Units of Weight and Measure, Miscellaneous Publication* 286, 79 pp. (Washington, National Bureau of Standards).

Clason, W. E. (1964) *Lexicon of International and National Units*, 76 pp. (Amsterdam, Elsevier).

CODATA (1969) Automated information handling in data centers, *CODATA Bull.*, no. 1 (Oct.), 12 pp.

CODATA (1970) Tentative set of key values for thermodynamics. Part I. Report of the ICSO—CODATA Task Group on Key Values for Thermodynamics. *CODATA Bull.*, no. 2 (Nov.), 6 pp.

CODATA (1971a) An announcement by the CODATA Task Group on Key Values for Thermodynamics. *J. Chem. Thermodyn.*, **3**(1), 1—6.

CODATA (1971b) A catalog of compilation and data evaluation activities in chemical kinetics, photochemistry and radiation chemistry. *CODATA Bull.*, no. 3 (Dec.), 28 pp.

CODATA (1971c) Automated information handling in data centers. *CODATA Bull.*, no.4 (Dec.), 12 pp.

CODATA (1971d) Final set of key values for thermodynamics. Part 1. Report of the CODATA Task Group on Key Values for Thermodynamics. *CODATA Bull.*, no. 6 (Dec.), 5 pp.

CODATA (1971e) Tentative set of key values for thermodynamics. Part 2. Report of the CODATA Task Group on Key Values for Thermodynamics. *CODATA Bull.*, no. 6 (Dec.), 8 pp.

CODATA (1972a) Report of the ICSU—CODATA Task Group on Key Values for Thermodynamics. *J. Chem. Thermodyn.*, **4**(3), 331-6.

CODATA (1972b) Tentative set of key values for thermodynamics. Part 3. Report of the CODATA Task Group on Key Values for Thermodynamics. *CODATA Bull.*, no. 7 (Aug.), 4 pp.

CODATA (1973a) *Proceeding of the 3rd International CODATA Conference on Generalization, Compilation and Dissemination of Data for Science and Technology*, Le Creusot, France, Aug. 1973, 100 pp. (Frankfurt/Main, CODATA Secretariat).

CODATA (1973b) Guide for the presentation in the primary literature of numerical data derived from experiments. *CODATA Bull.*, no. 9 (Dec.), 6 pp.

CODATA (1973c) CODATA recommended key values for thermodynamics, 1973. Report of the CODATA Task Group on Key Values for Thermodynamics. *CODATA Bull.*, no. 10 (Dec.), 12 pp.

CODATA (1973d) Recommended consistent values of the fundamental physical constants, 1973. *CODATA Bull.*, no. 11 (Dec.), 8 pp.

CODATA (1974a) Energy data accessing and/or retrieval. *CODATA Bull.*, no. 12, (Sept.), 12 pp.

CODATA (1974b) The presentation of chemical kinetics data in the primary literature. *CODATA Bull.*, no. 13 (Dec.), 8 pp.

CODATA (1975a) CODATA recommended key values for thermodynamics, 1973. Reports of the CODATA Task Group on Key Values for Thermodynamics. *J. Chem. Thermodyn.*, **7**(1), 1-3.

CODATA (1975b) Proceedings of the 4th International CODATA Conference on the Generation, Compilation, Evaluation and Dissemination of Data for Science and Technology. *CODATA Bull.*, no. 14 (Feb.), 171 pp.

CODATA (1975c) Man-machine communication in scientific data handling. *CODATA Bull.*, no. 15 (March), 32 pp.

CODATA (1975d) Study on the problems of accessibility and dissemination of data for science and technology. *CODATA Bull.*, no. 16 (Oct.), 32 pp.

CODATA (1976a) CODATA recommended key values for thermodynamics, 1975. Report of the CODATA Task Group on Key Values for Thermodynamics, 1975. *J. Chem. Thermodyn.*, **8**(7), 603-5.

CODATA (1976a) CODATA recommended key values for thermodynamics, 1975. *CODATA Bull.*, no. 17 (Jan.), 12 pp.

CODATA (1976b) Flagging and tagging data. *CODATA Bull.*, no. 19 (June), 22 pp.

CODATA (1976c) Recommendations for measurement and presentation of biochemical equilibrium data. *CODATA Bull.*, no. 20 (Sept.), 16 pp.

CODATA (1977a) CODATA recommended key values for thermodynamics, 1976. *CODATA Bull.*, no. 22 (March), 8 pp.

CODATA (1977b) Biologists' guide for the presentation of numerical data in the primary literature. *CODATA Bull.*, no. 25 (Nov.), 5 pp.

CODATA (1978a) CODATA recommended key values for thermodynamics, 1977. Report of the CODATA Task Group on Key Values for Thermodynamics, 1977. *J. Chem. Thermodyn.*, **10**(10), 903-6.

CODATA (1978b) CODATA recommended key values for thermodynamics, 1977. *CODATA Bull.*, no. 28 (Apr.), 17 pp.

CODATA (1978c) Selected papers on natural and man-made hazards and related questions from the 6th International CODATA Conference. *CODATA Bull.*, no. 29 (Nov.), 64 pp.

CODATA (1978d) Guide for the presentation in the primary literature of physical property correlation and estimation procedures. *CODATA Bull.*, no. 30 (Dec.), 6 pp.

CODATA (1979a) Data needs for energy. *CODATA Bull.*, no. 31, (March), 30 pp.

CODATA (1979b) Guide for the presentation in the primary literature of numerical data derived from observations in the geosciences. *CODATA Bull.*, no. 32 (Aug.), 6 pp.

CODATA (1979c) Evaluated kinetic and photochemical data for atmospheric chemistry. *CODATA Bull.*, no. 33 (Sept.), 16 pp.

CODATA (1980) Problems in the treatment of numerical data. *CODATA Bull.*, no. 39 (Dec.), 109 pp.

CODATA (1981) Calorimetric measurements on cellular systems, recommendations for measurements and presentation of results. *CODATA Bull.*, no. 44 (Aug.), 8 pp.

CODATA (1982a) An abridgement of evaluated kinetic and photochemical data for atmospheric chemistry. Supplement 1. *CODATA Bull.*, no. 45 (Jan.), 31 pp.

CODATA (1982b) Guide to the presentation of astronomical data, *CODATA Bull.*, no. 46 (Apr.), 9 pp.

CODATA (1982c) A systematic approach to the preparation of thermodynamic tables, *CODATA Bull.*, no. 47 (May), 13 pp.

CODATA (1983) Guide for the preparation of thermodynamic tables and correlations of the fluid state, *CODATA Bull.*, no. 51 (Dec.), 43 pp.

CODATA (1984a) Scientific program and abstracts. 9th International CODATA Conference, 24–28, June 1984, Jerusalem, Israel. *CODATA Bull.*, no. 54 (March), 89 pp.

CODATA (1984b) CODATA directory of data sources for science and technology. Chap. 11. Chemical Thermodynamics. *CODATA Bull.*, no. 55 (April), 125 pp.

Collins, J. C. (ed.) (1960) *Radioactive Wastes, Their Treatment and Disposal*, 239 pp. (London, E. & F. N. Spon).

Crane Ltd (1981) *Flow of Fluids through Valves, Fittings and Pipes*, Techn. Paper No. 410 M, 4 chap. (London, Crane Ltd).

Crichton, F. A. (1961) *Metric Systems with English Equivalents*, 15th edn, 80 pp. (Edinburgh, Gall & Inglis).

Davis, N. H. (1970) SI units for chemists. *Chem. Brit.*, **6**(8), 344–6.

Davies, N. H. (1971) SI electric and magnetic units for chemists. *Chem Brit.*, **7**(8), 331–2.

Dean, J. A. (ed.) (1979) *Lange's Handbook of Chemistry*, 12th edn. 11 chap. (New York, McGraw-Hill).

Drazil, J. V. (1971) *Dictionary of Quantities and Units*, 230 pp. (London, Leonard Hill).

Drazil, J. V. (1983) *Quantities and Units of Measurements. A Dictionary and Handbook*, 313 pp. (London, Mansell).

Dresner, S. (1971) *Units of Measurement. An Encyclopedic Dictionary*, 287 pp. (Aylesbury, Harvey Miller & Medcalf).

Ebert, H. (1976) *Physikalisches Taschenbuch*, 5th edn, 128 pp. (Braunschweig, Vieweg).

Ellis, B. (1966) *Basic Concepts of Measurements*, 64 pp. (Cambridge, Cambridge University Press).

Engineering Equipment Users Association (1971) *Recommended Metric Units for Use in Research Laboratories*, EEUA Document no. 41 D, 20 pp.

Engineering Sciences Data Unit (1968) *Introductory Memorandum of the Viscosity of Liquids and the Classification of Lubricating Oils*, Item no. 68036 (Oct.), 26 pp.

Flick, E. W. (ed.) (1985) *Industrial Solvents Handbook*, 3rd edn, 648 pp. (Park Ridge, Noyes).

Forsythe, W. E. (ed.) (1956) *Smithsonian Physical Tables*, 9th edn, 827 pp. (Washington, Smithsonian Institute).

Franke, H. (1969) *Lexikon der Physik*, 3rd edn, 3 vols, 1457 pp. (Stuttgart, Franckh'sche Verlagshandlung).

Glaeser, P. S. (ed.) (1980) Data for science and technology. *Proc. 7th International CODATA Conference, Kyoto Japan*, 615 pp. (Oxford, Pergamon Press).

Glaeser, P. S. (ed.) (1982) Data for science and technology. *Proc. 8th International CODATA Conference, Jachranka, Poland*, 350 pp. (Amsterdam, North Holland Publishing).

Goldsmith, A., Waterman, T. E. and Hirschborn, H. J. (1961) *Handbook of Thermophysical Properties of Solid Materials*, 5 vol., 752 + 1270 + 1162 + 798 + 286 pp. (New York, Macmillan).

Gordon, A. J. and Ford, R. A. (1972) *The Chemist's Companion. A Handbook of Practical Data, Techniques and References*, 537 pp. (New York, John Wiley).

Gori, G. (1985) The definition and symbols for the quantity called "molarity" or "concentration" and for the SI units of this quantity. *J. Chem. Educ.*, **62**(9), 741.

Gray, D. E. (ed.) (1963) *American Institute of Physics Handbook*, 2nd edn, 9 chap. (New York, McGraw-Hill).

Green, M. H. (1962) *International and Metric Units of Measurement*, 116 pp. (London, Heywood & Co.).

Grigull, U. and Sandner, H. (1984) *Heat Conduction*, 187 pp. (Berlin, Springer-Verlag).

Handley, W. (ed.) (1977) *Industrial Safety Handbook*, 2nd edn, 480 pp. (New York, McGraw-Hill).

Haywood, R. W. (1972) *Thermodynamic Tables in SI Units*, 2nd edn, 42 pp. (Cambridge, Cambridge University Press).

Holden, N. E. and Martin, R. L. (1984) Atomic weights of the elements, 1983. *Pure Appl. Chem.*, **56**(4), 653–74.

Hoppe, J. I. (1972) Dipole moments and SI. *Educ. Chem.*, **9**(4), 138–40.

Horvath, A. L. (1970) Specific resistance. *Electron. Power*, **16**(4), 141.

Horvath, A. L. (1975) *Physical Properties of Inorganic Compounds. SI Units.* 480 pp. (London, Edward Arnold).

Horvath, A. L. (1982) *Halogenated Hydrocarbons: Solubility—Miscibility with Water*, 889 pp. (New York, Marcel Dekker).

Horvath, A. L. (1985) *Handbook of Aqueous Electrolyte Solutions. Physical Properties, Estimation and Correlation Methods*, 631 pp. (Chichester, Ellis Horwood).

Horvath, A. L. (1986) *Chemical Structure Generation from the Properties of Pure Organic Compounds* (in preparation). (Amsterdam, Elsevier).

Horvath, A. L. and Getzen, F. W. (ed.) (1985) *IUPAC Solubility Data Series*, vol. 20, *Halogenated Benzenes, Toluenes and Phenols with Water*, 266 pp. (Oxford, Pergamon Press).

Hoy, K. L. (1970) New values of the solubility parameters from vapor pressure data. *J. Paint Technol.*, **42**(541), 76–118.

HTFS (1978) *Two-Dimensional Unit Conversion Charts*, Heat Transfer and Fluid Flow Services, 5 pp. (Harwell, AERE).

Hvistendahl, H. S. (1964) *Engineering Units and Physical Quantities*, 95 pp. (London, Macmillan).

International Standards (1979) *Quantities, Units, Symbols, Conversion Factors and Conversion Tables*, ISO 31 Series, Technological Committee ISO/TC 12, 14 parts. (Geneva, International Organization for Standardization).

International Union of Pure and Applied Physics (1978) Symbols, units and nomenclature in physics. *Physica*, **93A**, 1–60.

Jerrard, H. C. and McNeill, D. B. (1963) *A Dictionary of Scientific Units*, 197 pp. (London, Chapman & Hall).

Judson, L. V. (1955) *Units of Weight and Measure,*

Definitions and Tables of Equivalents, publication 214, (July 1), 196 pp. (Washington, National Bureau of Standards).

Kay, G. N. C. and Laby, T. H. (1973) *Physical and Chemical Constants*, 14th edn, 386 pp. (London, Longmans).

King, R. W. and Magid, J. (1979) *Industrial Hazard and Safety Handbook*, 793 pp. (London, Newnes-Butterworths).

Lacy, P. M. C. (1976) Two-dimensional energy conversion charts. *Chart. Mech. Engr* (June), 6–7.

Landolt-Börnstein (1951) Atom- und Molekularphysik, Molekeln II (Elektronenhülle), *Zahlenwerte und Funktionen aus Physik, Chemie, Astronomie, Geophysik und Technik*, vol. I, Part 3, 6th edn, 674 pp. (Berlin, Springer-Verlag).

Landolt-Börnstein (1974–) *Zahlenwerte und Funktionen aus Physik, Chemie, Astronomie, Geophysik und Technik*, neue Serie. (Berlin, Springer-Verlag).

Lax, E. and Synowietz, C. (ed.) (1964–1970) *Taschenbuch fur Chemiker und Physiker*, 3rd edn, 3 vol., 1522 + 1177 + 670 pp. (Berlin, Springer-Verlag).

Le Neindre, B. and Vodar, B. (ed.) (1975) *Experimental Thermodynamics*, vol. II, 1318 pp. (London, Butterworths).

Lowe, D. A. (1975) A guide to international recommendation on names, symbols for quantities and on units of measurement. Progress in standardization: 2, *Bull. WHO* **52**, suppl., 314–90.

McGlasham, M. L. (ed.) (1970) *Manual of Symbols and Terminology for Physicochemical Quantities and Units, IUPAC Division of Physical Chemistry*, 44 pp. (London, Butterworths).

McGlasham, M. L. (1971) *Physicochemical Quantities and Units. The Grammar and Spelling of Physical Chemistry*, 2nd edn, 117 pp. (London, Royal Institute of Chemistry).

Mackay, D. and Shiu, W. Y. (1981) A critical review of Henry's law constants for chemicals of enviromental interest. *J. Phys. Chem. Ref. Data*, **10**(4), 1175–99.

McWeeny, R. (1973) Natural units in atomic and molecular physics, *Nature*, **243**(5404), 196–8.

Maglic, K. D., Cezairliyan, A. and Peletsky, V. E. (ed.) (1984) *Compendium of Thermophysical Property Measurement Methods*. vol. 1. Survey of Measurement Techniques, Plenum, New York, 789 pp.

Mayhew, Y. R. and Rogers, G. F. C. (1977) *Thermodynamic and Transport Properties of Fluids. SI Units*. 2nd edn, 20 pp. (Oxford, Blackwell).

Melhuish, W. H. (1984). VI. Molecular luminescence spectroscopy. Nomenclature, symbols, units and their usage in spectrochemical analysis. *Pure Appl. Chem.*, **56**(2), 231–45.

Melhuish, W. H. and Zander, M. (1981) Nomenclature, symbols, units and their usage in spectrochemical analysis. VI. Molecular luminescence spectroscopy, *Pure Appl. Chem.*, **53**(6), 1953–66.

Metrication Board (1977) *How to Write Metric. A Style Guide for Teaching and Using SI Units*, 36 pp. (London, HMSO).

Morgan, M. and Kirk, W. E. (1971) Calculations in SI Units. *Educ. Chem.*, **8**(2), 50–53.

Mullin, J. W. (1971) Recent developments in the change-over to the international system of units (SI). *Chem. Engr (London)*, (254), 352–6.

Mullin, J. W. (1972) SI Units in chemical engineering, *AIChE Journal*, **18**(1), 222–4.

Mullin, J. W. (1973) Solution concentration and supersaturation. Units and their conversion factors, *Chem. Engr (London)*, (274), 316–7.

National Bureau of Standards (1967) *ASTM Metric Practice Guide*, Handbook 102, 236 pp. (Washington, National Bureau of Standards).

National Bureau of Standards (1971) Policy for NBS usage of SI units. *J.Chem. Educ.*, **48**(9), 569–72.

National Bureau of Standards (1982) *Model State Laws and Regulations*, Handbook 130, 104 pp. (Washington, National Bureau of Standards).

National Physical Laboratory (1969) *Changing to the Metric System. Conversion Factors, Symbols and Definitions*, 48 pp. (London, HMSO).

Norris, A. C. (1971) SI Units in Physico-Chemical Calculations. *J. Chem. Educ.*, **48**(12), 797–800.

Oldshue, J. Y. (1981). AIChE goes metric. *AIChE Journal*, **27**(1), 1–4.

Padelt, E. and Laporte, H. (1976) *Enheiten und Grösenarten der Naturwissenschaften*, 89 pp. (Leipzig, VEB Fachbuchverlag).

Page, C. H. and Vigoureux, P. (ed.) (1972) *SI. The International System of Units*, NBS Special Publication 330, 45 pp. (Washington, National Bureau of Standards).

Page, C. H. and Vigoureux, P. (ed.) (1973) *SI. The International System of Units*, 47 pp. (London, HMSO).

Pankhurst, R. C. (1964) *Dimensional Analysis and Scale Factors*, 132 pp. (London, Chapman & Hall).

Parrish, A. (ed.) (1973) *Mechanical Engineer's Reference Book*, 20 chap. (London, Butterworths).

Paul, M. A. (1971) The international system of units (SI), development and progress. *J. Chem. Docum.*, **11**(1), 3–8.

Peiser, H. S. (1985) How good are the standard atomic weights? *Anal. Chem.*, **57**(4), 511A–22A.

Perry, J. H. and Green, D. W. (ed.) (1985) *Chemical Engineers' Handbook*, 6th edn, 2336 pp. (New York, McGraw-Hill).

Pullen, W. W. F. (1978) *Engineering Tables and Data*, 8th edn, 95 pp. (Manchester, Scientific Publishing Co.).

Qasim, S. H. (1977) *SI Units in Engineering and Technology*, 54 pp. (Oxford, Pergamon Press).

Quayle, J. P. (ed.) (1985) *Kempe's Engineers Year-Book 1985*, London, 79 chap. (London, Morgan-Grampian).

Rossini, F. D. (1974) *Fundamental Measures and Constants for Science and Technology*, 132 pp. (Cleveland, The Chemical Rubber Co.).

Rossini, F. D., Wagman, D. D., Evans, W. H., Levine, S. and Jaffe, I. (1952) *Selected Values of Chemical Thermodynamic Properties*, Circular no. 500, 1266 pp. (Washington, National Bureau of Standards).

Rossmassler, S. A. (1967) The National Standard Reference Data System Program in atomic and molecular properties. *J. Chem. Docum.*, **7**(1), 15–18.

Rossmassler, S. A. and Watson, D. G. (ed.) (1980) *Data Handling for Science and Technology. An Overview and Sourcebook*, 347 pp. (Amsterdam, North Holland Publishing).

Royal Society (1971) *Quantities, Units and Symbols*, 48 pp. (London, Royal Society).

Sacklowski, A. (1979) *Die neuen SI-Einheiten*, 86 pp.

(Munich, Goldmann).

Schweitzer, P. A. (ed.) (1979) *Handbook of Separation Techniques for Chemical Engineers*, 6 chap. (New York, McGraw-Hill).

Sheppard, N., Willis, H. A. and Rigg, J. C. (1985) Names, symbols, definitions and units of quantities in optical spectroscopy. *Pure Appl. Chem.*, **57**(1), 105–20.

Siggaard-Andersen, O., Durst, R. A. and Maas, A. H. J. (1984) Physicochemical quantities and units in clinical chemistry with special emphasis on activities and activity coefficients. *Pure Appl. Chem.*, **56**(5), 567–94.

Spiers, H. M. (ed.) (1961). *Technical Data on Fuel*. 6th edn, 360 pp. (London, British National Committee of the World Power Conference).

Steere, N. V. (ed.) (1967) *Handbook of Laboratory Safety*. 568 pp. (Cleveland, The Chemical Rubber Co.).

Strasheim, A. (1981) Nomenclature, symbols, units and their usage in spectrochemical analysis. V. Radiation sources. *Pure Appl. Chem.*, **53**(6), 1913–52.

Stull, D. R. and Prophet, H. (1971) *JANAF Thermochemical Tables*, 2nd edn, NSRDS-NBS 37, 1141 pp. (Washington, National Bureau of Standards).

Stull, D. R., Westrum, E. F. and Sinke, G. C. (1969) *The Chemical Thermodynamics of Organic Compounds*, 865 pp. (New York, John Wiley).

Touloukian, Y. S., Liley, P. E. and Saxena, S. C. (1970) *Thermophysical Properties of Matter*, vol. 3, *Thermal Conductivity. Nonmetallic Liquids and Gases*, 531 pp. (New York, IFI/Plenum Press).

Touloukian, Y. S. and Makita, T. (1970) *Thermophysical Properties of Matter*, vol. 6, *Specific Heat. Nonmetallic Liquids and Gases*, 312 pp. (New York, IFI/Plenum Press).

Touloukian, Y. S., Saxena, S. C. and Hestermans, P. (1975) *Thermophysical Properties of Matter*, vol. 11, *Viscosity*, 643 pp. (New York, IFI/Plenum Press).

Wagman, D. D., Evans, W. H., Parker, V. B., Schumm, R. H., Halow, I., Bailey, S. M., Churney, K. L. and Nuttall, R. L. (1982) Selected values for inorganic and C_1 and C_2 organic substances in SI units. *J. Phys. Chem. Ref. Data*, **11,** suppl. no. 2, 392 pp.

Weast, R. C. (ed.) (1985) *CRC Handbook of Chemistry and Physics*, 66th edn, 2384 pp. (Boca Raton, CRC Press).

Weast, R. C. and Astle, M. J. (ed.) (1985) *CRC Handbook of Data on Organic Compounds*, 2 vol., 1936 pp. (Boca Raton, CRC Press).

Whiffen, D. H. (ed.) (1979) Manual of symbols and terminology for physicochemical quantities and units, *Pure Appl. Chem.*, **51**(1), 1-41.

Wilhoit, R. C. and Zwolinski, B. J. (1971) *Handbook of Vapor Pressures and Heats of Vaporization of Hydrocarbons and Related Compounds*. 329 pp. (A & M University, Texas, Thermodynamic Research Center).

Young, L. (1969) *System of Units in Electricity and Magnetism*, 126 pp. (Edinburgh, Oliver & Boyd).

Index